Ted Parratt is a journalist and former laboratory technician who has been researching the subject of drink additives for some years.

His interest in drinks and drinking began when, as a small boy in a Surrey village, he regularly helped his grandfather to make cider. Thirty or more years later, when he was working on an electronics journal, his editorial colleagues began to raise questions concerning drinks which he found difficult to answer. Gradually, he came to realize that where information on drinks was available it was either inadequate or buried in official reports. *Name Your Poison!* is the result of four years of research conducted as a consequence of his desire to learn more about what goes through the consumer's mouth and into the stomach. Among his other interests are food, books and music – he is an enthusiastic jazz guitarist, often playing alongside his son, one of his three grown-up children. He also has four grandchildren. Ted Parratt is now a newspaper journalist working in Surrey.

GW00647305

# Name Your Poison!

*A Guide to Additives in Drinks*

TED PARRATT

Chris.
Keep on producing those thirst-
quenching poisons, and avoid
Coke like you would Listerine.

Ted

ROBERT HALE · LONDON

Robert Hale Limited
Clerkenwell House
Clerkenwell Green
London EC1R 0HT

**British Library Cataloguing in Publication Data**

Parratt, Ted
  Name your poison!
  1. Alcoholic drinks. Additives
  I. Title
  663'.11

  ISBN 0–7090–4054–7

Set in Palatino by
Derek Doyle & Associates, Mold, Clwyd.
Printed in Great Britain by
St Edmundsbury Press Ltd, Bury St Edmunds, Suffolk.
Bound by WBC Bookbinders Limited.

# Contents

To my late cousin, Frank 'Punch' Parratt,
who died before this book was completed.
He drank well, but wisely, for eighty-four years.

# Diagrams

Artwork drawn by EDANART.

# Acknowledgements

The many comments about drinks I have heard in bars, public houses and restaurants during the thirty years I have been a drinker were prime movers among my reasons for writing this book.

Some of those comments were amusing, some were illuminating, but most were spectacularly ill-informed, which prompted my search for answers to fill the more important information gaps. With the growth of the promotion of chemically dubious non-alcoholic drinks as 'healthy' contrasting so acutely with the ambiguous attitudes to alcohol of some doctors, I set out to eliminate confusion, if only for my own and my family's benefit. That confusion, which is widespread in Britain and Europe especially, is concerned with the essential ingredients and methods of drinks-production, and my aim in clarifying these issues has been to produce a useful body of information which could act as a reference to drinks in general as well as a means of identifying safer alternatives.

While I am grateful to all the voluble lounge lizards, boozy bar-stool philosophers and ordinary drinkers who have wittingly or unwittingly contributed material, I am especially grateful to the following people, who provided essential advice and information:

## Britain

Maxwell Laurie (T.A. Cutbill & Partners – for Wine and Spirit Association), Brian Bacon and Phil Ashton (Munton & Fison plc), Dr Tim Lang (London Food Commission), Ron Brown (Scotch Whisky Association), Dr David Long (Brewers' Society), Richard Swinhoe (Fuller Smith & Turner plc), Ian Draper (Safeway Foodstores Ltd), John Withey (Shepherd Neame), the staff of the Food Standards Division, MAFF, Jerry Schooler and Peter Arguil (Lurgashall Winery), Ian Muir (Coca-Cola Great Britain), John Dennis (Hartridge & Sons Ltd).

## USA

Richard Mascolo (Bureau of Alcohol, Tobacco and Firearms), Dr Michael Jacobson (Center for Science in the Public Interest).

# Foreword by Dr Tim Lang

Director, London Food Commission

Everyone has the legal right to expect their food and drink to be safe. Alas, in the 1980s food safety became a hot issue because expectations of safety were not always being met.

Since the 1960s there has been a growth of well-informed, independent research organizations serving the public – consumer groups, environmental groups and health groups. What might be called 'active consumerism' has become a feature of our society. This new consumerism demands more information about what goes in, on and around food and drink so that we the public can judge the product, choose what we like, and not just buy what we are sold. As a result, access to information about food and drink has become a point of hot contention at times.

This new active consumerism is sometimes bitterly attacked by governments and industry interests who have even accused consumer groups of a wrecking approach to industry! Such charges are patently absurd. A few maverick extortionists or attention-seekers aside, it is not consumers who adulterate foods. Too often, alas, adulteration is routine and sometimes even legal.

A theme of the 1990s is said to be 'quality of life'. Certainly quality of food and drink are now firmly on the agenda for the decade. Information – and the tussle to make it open rather than secret – lies at the heart of this quality debate. If only government, industry and regulatory bodies would take the initiative and declare more. In my experience, a mess often ensures that secrecy rules. Competition within the industry means it won't volunteer information. Government won't act as honest broker for the public interest because it doesn't want to upset trade, and regulatory committees are pathetically under-resourced and lack vision or will. Every day, we the public drink and eat the results of this unnecessary policy mess.

At a time when we might have hoped for an information explosion from government or industry, there is only a trickle, and that is too often only the result of pressure from outside consumer groups and researchers. It really is quite ludicrous that enquiries by individuals seeking information on ingredients or additives which we all ingest are too often met with a wall of silence.

This book is about a subject which has received only limited coverage in the UK. The book is a testament to one citizen's investigation and persistence. It is depressing, but not altogether unexpected I have to confess, to learn that with one or two exceptions the author has met obstruction and evasion where questions about practice and safety within the drinks industry have been raised. The drinks industry is famously powerful, politically well-connected and ruthlessly competitive. How surprising, then, that no one in the industry has broken ranks and started giving more information. In food, this happened in the 1980s.

Roll on the day when big retailers take a lead and give full ingredients detail on their own-label drinks. Roll on the day when the big buyers ask their suppliers for the same. Whether their motive would be self-interest or genuine concern to meet the consumer's right to know in some respects doesn't matter at this time. The case this book makes is the urgency of beginning the debate in the UK. Why, if I go to the USA, am I told on a wine bottle whether the wine contains sulphites? Because a well-organized and researched case built up pressure to force this sensible innovation on the industry. It is time we in Europe shared the gains made in the USA for those who wish or need to avoid sulphites.

1992 and its removal of barriers to trade within the European Economic Community would win more public support if it brought a raising of standards for consumers, not just a passport to trade. I note with interest that some higher standards of beer in Germany, for instance, are now being undermined by 1992 regulations. Am I alone in pitying poor Germany if it suffers some of our beer standards?

Since the 1989 food scandals, the Government has had to institute some changes. Some can be welcomed; others are cosmetic. On many key issues in food policy there is a deafening silence. In the 1990s pressure will have to be kept up by organizations and, equally importantly, by all of us as individual shoppers. A letter to the supermarket chairman or a talk to the store manager can work wonders.

Drinks are important. Our bodies need liquid. Our culture and history have given us a vast range of drinks, some of them alcoholic. New technologies and processes from the chemistry and product development laboratories are bringing on-stream ever more products. The globe is being raided for new recipes, concoctions and brands to tickle our taste-buds. We are the guinea-pigs. Fine, you might say, as long as I know. The point this book makes is that too often you and we don't.

The public health advice, please remember, is that we should restrict our consumption of alcohol, but as this book shows, drinks are a veritable cocktail of ingredients, some unexpected. That is why the exclusion of drinks from labelling requirements is not just regrettable, but downright scandalous.

This book provides more than information. It lays down a challenge to producers and regulators alike. If history is repeated it will take more pressure from the public and independent organizations to make those with power over drinks see some sense.

Tim Lang
London
January 1990

# WELL-KEPT SECRETS

# Introduction

You can't judge a book by its cover, and you certainly can't judge a drink by the label on its container, because the information essential to such a judgement is missing from all alcoholic drinks stories and many non-alcoholic drinks stories. They have no comprehensive 'contents page' and are unlikely ever to acquire such a vital feature.

Strange though it may seem, hardly anyone ever drinks alcohol. Some people 'enjoy a snifter', others 'sample the occasional bevvy', while still others 'down a swift half', but if these and other euphemistic expressions indicate anything significant, it is that few people openly admit to a passion for alcohol or the many famous fluids in which it appears.

Unless you abstain for medical or religious reasons or have been a lifetime teetotaller from choice, you are among the ninety per cent of adults in Britain, Europe and the USA who drink. As a result, you may recognize these euphemisms for what they are: tongue-in-cheek comments which conceal a physical intimacy with the most sociable, yet often the most anti-social, of fluids – the substance which chemists and biologists define as $C_2H_5OH$, but which we all know as alcohol.

There are many good reasons for drinking, and one's just entered my head:
If I can't drink when I'm living, how can I drink when I'm dead?

The question in the last line of this old verse points to drinking as enjoyment and not as a source of life-threatening problems. Its theme bears witness to a centuries-old love affair between the human race and booze. As in other affairs, many of the loved-one's faults are ignored or brushed aside – we tend to play

11

down the more risky implications of the beloved drug, for fear of missing out on the glamorous lifestyle which drinks-advertisers suggest will flow from consumption of their products – a person is considered incomplete without the right drinking image.

There is a darker, less public side to drinking. Not only has alcohol consumption steadily increased over the years but during the last twenty a revolution has taken place in the way in which most drinks, both alcoholic and non-alcoholic, are produced.

The immediately obvious 'bad' effects of abuse, such as hangovers, and possible long-term risks to health may be due partly to the additives and processing aids (mainly preservatives) which remain in drinks. WHEN COMBINED WITH ALCOHOL, THESE MAY POSE A DOUBLE THREAT. In spite of this growing risk, however, some of the most habitually compelling substances are being drunk by 'blindfolded' consumers, because although many dry foods are now labelled to show their ingredients, drinkers are still not permitted to know what their favourite drinks contain.

Much of the data drinkers need to judge the dangers is not available, and that material which is issued is filtered by food-producers and advisory committees. Therefore, where we need to know more, we are given less, although it is true to say that there has been some progress in the consumer's battle to discover exactly what is being eaten and drunk, due to the pressure of public opinion, the effects of British membership of the EEC and the increasing thrust of some health and food pressure groups.

Some food-producers, aware of the growing energy of the 'green' movement, which all political parties are keen to be seen embracing, are limiting additives in their products. Monosodium glutamate, a flavour-enhancer which is used extensively in Chinese restaurants worldwide, does not appear as often on food labels, though it may be that less familiar enhancers, such as sodium ribonucleotide, are replacing 'MSG', which is invariably included in stock cubes and soup mixes.

A few producers have returned to the use of natural spices and sauces to boost flavour, even though their endeavours may be intended only to gain the publicity edge over food-campaigners. They know that by describing their products as containing 'no artificial colours or preservatives' they may well sell more of them because of a general public perception of 'artificial additives' as undesirable or even dangerous. This is not necessarily a valid conclusion: some natural colouring materials are not necessarily safer than their artificial counterparts. E100 curcumin, for example, a colouring matter derived from the Indian rhizome (spicy root) turmeric, is under investigation to discover why pigs fed the yellow colour material under a test programme suffered an increase in thyroid gland weight. E100 is added to many foods, including ice-cream.

The supermarkets represent one area where the influence of so-called 'organic foods' has been most marked. The former 'cranks' who wasted the time of foodstore managers with their constant harping about 'real foods' and 'high-fibre foods' and dismissive undertones about 'refined foods' are now seen as discerning customers, with real money to spend. In Britain, Europe and the USA demands are growing for concerted action on world environmental issues such as the protection of the Brazilian rainforests, and prevention of damage to the ozone layer in the atmosphere by components of aerosol sprays and refrigerant fluids, and emotive issues such as the effect of chemical waste on seals, but there is an important issue closer to home, where consumers are kept in the dark and denied information needed to make intelligent choices.

Unlike most dry foodstuffs, ALCOHOLIC DRINKS NEED NOT BE LABELLED TO SHOW THEIR INGREDIENTS.

The result is that only scant information is available to consumers of full-strength drinks as to their ingredients or possible health effects, most drinks carrying nothing more than an alcohol-content figure and a decorative label providing the 'image' name of the drink and the maker's name and address.

This latter detail is often misleading, because throughout the world it is the large brewery and winemaking combines which control most of the drinks-production. In Britain, for example, eight large brewery groups control the principal beer, cider and spirit drinks brands.

With the exception of those small (boutique) brewers who use no additives in their beers, who are listed in chapter 3 and those winemakers who are listed in chapter 5 as part of a world guide to organic wines, most manufacturers produce 'refined' drinks, which have been processed in such a way as to render them nutritionally valueless, except for their carbohydrate content.

One additive in particular, the preservative sulphur dioxide (E220) destroys vitamin $B_1$ (thiamin) and probably enhances the more painful effects of a severe hangover. This substance or one of its six variant forms is present in most beers (i.e. ales, lagers and stouts), ciders and wines throughout the world.

## All Quiet on the Manufacturing Front

The destructive processing of most drinks may be one good reason why producers resist the ingredient labelling of their brands. That his beer has been converted into a 'junk food' version or that his wine contains substances which the average vegetarian or vegan would avoid were he to be told about them (egg albumen, dried ox-blood powder, casein from cow's milk and gelatin, which is derived from animal bones are all used as clarifying – 'fining' – agents) is not something a producer would seek to advertise.

Should the labelling of drinks to show ingredients ever become a reality though, producers could be expected to rally to the challenge as they have with other foodstuff labels, to exploit the medium: 'Contains no arsenic' or 'High fluid content to aid kidney function' or even an off-beat message such as 'Ten-year-old tawny taste-bud killer, with built-in liver trauma'.

The most common (and conventional) industrial objections to ingredient-listing include the response that to itemize all the substances present (showing that there are many) would cause space problems on the bottle and push up the price of the drink. One 'authority' on the subject went so far as to express the opinion that to provide such information might cause stress problems for the consumer.

Dr Reg Passmore of Edinburgh University, who has served on several food advisory committees, including the COMA (Committee on Medical Aspects of Food Policy) in the 1970s, as well as on the FSC (Food Standards Committee), focused on this aspect of the industry's resistance to further labelling when in 1984, he wrote in a British Nutrition Foundation bulletin: 'Providing such information presents many difficulties for manufacturers and would inevitably put up prices; it would also probably increase the already large number of neurotics who worry unnecessarily about their food.' No doubt these 'neurotics' are the same silly people who have been worrying 'unnecessarily' about salmonella and listeria infection, outbreaks of botulism and legionnaires' disease, and BSE ('mad cow disease'), but the unsympathetic professor's message is clear: rather than give these fools data which might worry them, they should be protected from the unspeakable neurosis-inducing dangers of the informative label of ingredients. Manufacturers are happy to provide this 'consumer-protection' service, which has a convenient by-product: confidentiality for the food-producer.

In Britain the drinks-producer is free to act with no more apparent accountability to the consumer than the 1955 Food and Drugs Act requires: that he include nothing 'to render the food injurious to health'. Imagine a label based upon this criterion: 'No unprotected circular saws contained in this drink' or 'Rattlesnakes excluded'. Injurious materials are nowhere defined in the Act.

That his products may contain traces of arsenic or formaldehyde, as well as vitamin-destroying 'ingredients', does not appear to come under the control of the Act, since they may be by-products of fermentation or distillation and have not been deliberately included, i.e. there was no *intention* to include anything dangerous. An identical loophole exists in the Food Safety Act 1990.

The Food Labelling Regulations, which exclude full-strength alcoholic drinks from ingredient-labelling, became law in Britain in 1986, following five years of derogation by the British government. The European Directive of 1978 was not acted upon in Britain until 1984.

'Derogation' means the exercising of the right of any EEC member state, after agreement in council, to decline to implement directives within its own national borders. To some extent, though, the derogation process will continue to be irrelevant to the issue of labels for alcoholic drinks, because EEC regulations also exclude them from ingredient-labelling, except for alcohol-content.

Furthermore, Britain's move into the 'greater trading Europe' in 1992 is likely to have little effect upon the issue, because most other member states approve as many additives to drinks as do British authorities, except in Germany and the Benelux countries, where quasi-compulsory beer purity laws are in force.

In Britain, the 'mother of parliaments', democracy does not

extend to freedom of information for consumers. It seems almost laughable that the communication of details between food-producers and advisory committees is an official secret, especially if it is only the vitamin-enriching of ready-salted Golden Sunrise Crisps (excellent for promoting a thirst!) or the colour of the new packaging of the special camel- and aardvark-flavour variety that is being passed on, but since this is hardly likely to be the case, we must conclude that there are other reasons.

Could it be that producers (and influential investors) fear the effect on investment and profit should details of some of the materials they employ be made public? This book will be a disappointment to them if that is so, because many such substances are detailed here.

There are attempts to open up the British producers' cans of worms. Jonathan Aitken MP, the chairman of the Campaign for Freedom of Information's Parliamentary Liaison Committee, is one of the people who are trying to throw light on the subject. In May 1985 he addressed a Parliamentary Question to the Minister of Agriculture, Michael Jopling, who at the time had responsibility for the MAFF (the Ministry of Agriculture, Fisheries and Food) the regulatory authority: 'Will my honourable Friend explain why the nutritionists and other experts who serve on committees to do with food labelling, such as the Committee on Medical Aspects of Food Policy, are required to sign the Official Secrets Act? Is food labelling not a subject where maximum publicity is needed, not maximum security?'

Peggy Fenner, replying for the MAFF said: 'Food labelling is of course an issue on which the Food Advisory Committee advise the government rather than the Committee on Medical Aspects of Food Policy. Nevertheless, the principle is the same for the membership of both committees in that members are required to sign the Official Secrets Act.'

Although the transmission of data between food agencies and the producers is subject to the Official Secrets Act, the data itself – i.e. material concerning additives and ingredients of drinks – is not.

## To Add or Not to Add? That is the Question

There has always been a natural conflict between the food-producer and the consumer. The consumer expects fresh food, with all its flavour and nutrient benefits, but the producer cannot, except within certain constraints of cost and transport facilities, provide it. This is because the producer is subject to a natural commercial disadvantage, which is part of the inherent nature of fresh foods – they don't stay fresh for long if left unattended. In fresh foodstuffs of all kinds, their 'goodness' is transient – they tend to deteriorate very quickly, due to the action of airborne bacteria and fungi, unless they are treated in order to arrest the resulting decay.

As a result, food-manufacturers (who during two world wars were often applauded for providing good, wholesome food for both the military and civilian populations) see no good reason to return to natural, unprocessed foods because they know very well that their great commercial successes have been those foods which remain in good condition for a long time. This seems reasonable. Company directors can be expected to take action to maintain their commercial viability, which in turn maintains employment in the industry; but the Second World War is a long way away, and opinion on the links between food and health has now polarized, as a result of determined efforts to root out the information.

The increasingly vocal food-campaigner has put further pressure on the natural conflict, poking into dark political and commercial corners for both a fairer and a healthier deal.

Industrial backlash has become evident in strident propaganda from the food chains and their consultants, who are often professors of microbiology or chemistry, working at 'pure science', but who, upon close inspection, turn out to have former employment or funding links with food-producers.

One press release issued in 1985, soon after complaints that the new British labelling regulations were virtually toothless because they contained so many loopholes for the imaginative copywriters of the producers to exploit, referred to campaigners against refined sugars as 'food Leninists'. The statement backed Professor Vincent Marks who has often spoken at lectures organized by the Sugar Bureau.

The 'long-life' nature of dry foods stands in marked contrast with that of natural foods, which are growing in popularity as the 'green' spirit develops greater force, but only in the case of real ale is the 'green' drink of any real commercial significance. Except for vintage wines and spirits, however, the 'natural' image for drinks is likely to gain ground, especially when drinkers begin to realize that the CAMRA's (Campaign for Real Ale) success is bringing about a return to widescale brewing of real ales means they have a healthy choice of long drinks, as opposed to wines and spirits, which, like most refined foods, are virtually ruined by processing in all respects but the cosmetic.

The answer to the question 'To add or not to add?' is therefore: 'Yes, but only for commercial reasons' – additives favour the producer and the retailer but not the drinker. Preservatives are, however, vitally necessary in many cooked, processed foods.

There is another relevant contrast between dry foods and drinks, in their refined and natural forms. While experienced chefs and home-based cooks know how to select appropriate materials for economy and health, even they do not possess the basic recipe or materials knowledge to make an intelligent choice of drinks. This is because the vast majority of drinks are PRODUCED INDUSTRIALLY AND NOT IN THE HOME.

There is now virtually no tuition in brewing or winemaking skills to compare with the situation in William Cobbett's time, for example, when most rural nineteenth-century households brewed their own beer. Only in the small wine clubs and home-brewing societies is there anything remotely similar.

The kitchen-based nature of the two crafts clearly lends itself to DIY techniques, but the essential information is mainly in the hands of the big industrial producer, who not only refuses to pass on the benefits of his knowledge but continues to resist calls for information to be provided on ingredient labels.

The two most common industrial objections are:
(1) Many wines are the blended product of several winemakers, so listing would prove impractical.
(2) There is insufficient space on most labels for ingredient details.

It should prove no more difficult for wine-blenders or dealers to provide basic information to be included in a single label than it is for the many firms which prepare dry foods from basic components produced elsewhere. Examples are dried onion, potato starch and hydrolized yeast protein, all of which are listed on soups, sauces and other ready meals.

Wine bottles usually carry only one label, with the 'reverse' left clear or used to explain a history of the vineyard. On some wines there is also a map of the region of origin. Ingredient details could replace these labels, and the overall effect of having to publicize details would force down the amount of additives used, as well as bringing savings in the high cost of these substances for the producer.

The result could be the emergence of a new 'pure wine' elite; makers would compete to produce wine using fewer and fewer additives – surely a recipe for commercial success? Labels would not need to show all chemical materials, only the main ingredients and additives.

Further possibilities include labels which proclaim: 'Low alcohol, no additives' or 'Fermented solely from grape juice' or even, taking the bull firmly by the horns, 'Reduced hangover potential', where preservatives such as sulphur dioxide and benzoic acid are excluded. An environmental advantage would also accrue: should winemakers gradually return to organic growth methods, levels of nitrate contamination of soil and water supplies, which are affected as much by viticulture as by barley- and hop-growing for brewing, would fall.

An elderly cousin of mine, who was known to favour the odd one or two pints at a session, often remarked while drinking: 'I'll be glad when I've had enough of this.' He was a cautious drinker, but most consumers have no way of deciding exactly how much is enough for a shocker of a hangover should they shift from beer to red wine and back again during an evening. Only the bags under the eyes and the 'better-off dead' expression the next day tell the tale of chemical miscalculation and self-inflicted wounds.

Most of the hangover-inducing ingredients of drinks are unnecessary to their manufacture. In fact, the production of natural, fairly healthy beverages, in which the most dangerous element is the alcohol they contain, is anything but technical and can be understood by anyone who is capable of following a recipe for soup.

The industrial drinks process, in contrast, employs additives at virtually every stage, as the flow diagrams in each drinks section indicate. Production is followed up by high-powered image-marketing of drinks, where, for example, lager has been promoted as a strongly masculine long drink. Such advertising techniques outline the apparent benefits to drinkers of a vast range of liquid assets in cans, bottles, casks and kegs. You might think that, with such positive marketing, there would be plenty of publically available data concerning the drinks themselves, but drinkers' questions usually meet dead ends. 'It's probably a bit too technical for you to understand' is the most common patronizing reply from producers, and if this fails to deter: 'We can't tell you anything – it's a trade secret.'

In Britain, the USA and most EEC member states, therefore, it can be concluded that solid or dry foods are partially covered by labelling needs but that *nowhere in the northern hemisphere is there adequate or informative ingredient-listing of alcoholic drinks.*

The drinker is confined to making purely an educated guess about the ingredients, the food value and the possible long-term health effects of consuming his or her favourite drink. Further, such drinkers can make no reliable decisions about the chance of hangovers or other nasty effects in the absence of this information.

In the USA in 1987, campaigners pushing legislation planned six years earlier, which would have made it compulsory for wine-producers to list on the bottle any sulphites their wine contained, suffered an initial setback when the Reagan administration closed down the agency responsible.

Their efforts have been rewarded, however, because new legislation enacted early in 1989 meant that from March of that year all USA-made alcoholic drinks have had to carry not only a 'health dangers of alcohol' warning, much like those on cigarette packets ('Smoking can cause fatal diseases'), but, also a 'contains sulphites' warning. This has been implemented by Californian wine-producers, but wine-shippers and retailers in Britain and Europe are FREE TO OBSCURE THESE DETAILS ON THE LABEL WITH ANOTHER LABEL, and some are doing so. At least six people in the US are known to have died as a result of consuming sulphites, which may trigger asthmatic attacks.*

General ingredient-labelling appears to be advancing most quickly in Australia, where wines must indicate the presence of

* There are 2 million asthma sufferers in Britain, according to Asthma Society figures. It is estimated that about 2,000 are 'at risk' from elements of diet. See Appendix 2: E220 sulphur dioxide.

any preservatives. No such moves are planned for Britain, nor for any other EEC country, although as from July 1989 all British and European (i.e. EEC-controlled) producers of alcoholic drinks have been required to list each drink's alcohol content in a public place on the premises. While they are doing that, it would make sense to indicate the number of alcohol units each container/drink holds.

## Signposts

That old rhyme about drinking while one is alive rather than dead is a bit daft, but it serves to emphasize human fascination with alcoholic drinks. For some drinkers, though, the enjoyment felt in downing the favoured tipple has become modified by concern over the health consequences of the drinking-habit.

In spite of such fears, regular drinkers often do not stick to new regimes of temperance and return to their qld drinking-habits. This is hardly surprising in view of the widespread confusion which results from contradictory reports stressing the benefits (or the dangers) of alcohol in the diet, much of the confusion compounded by doctors who say the habit is dangerous (and stress that in 1988 there were a million people suffering with alcohol-related diseases) but conclude by saying that they enjoy a drink themselves.

These responses are echoes of the dichotomy relevant to tobacco-smoking: that the state cannot afford to lose the revenue derived from habit-forming consumables, yet must pay for the ill-health they may generate if abused. None of these approaches is of much practical use for the confused drinker, who could benefit from information about the safer 'middle road' which can be pursued through cautious, informed drinking.

The path to healthy, enjoyable imbibing is badly signposted, and the enquiring drinker must learn to interpret much 'encoded' information from many sources if the drinking good life is to last into the drinking long life.

Sensible drinking can bring benefits, such as the relief of stress, a dangerous factor in the modern world of business in particular. It has been said that cautious drinking (no more than two units per day) can help to reduce blood pressure a little, but it must be emphasized that moderate to heavy drinking is likely to increase it.

The health benefits generally, however, are not all that easy to isolate, partly because of the many strange substances which go into modern drinks, for little is known about their likely long-term effects. Since research is virtually confined to work on the effects of alcohol, and not upon possible synergistic effects (where two or more substances react to produce an effect not created by the substances singly), it is only by informed and cautious drinking behaviour that the consumer can hope to outweigh any possible risks.

The subject of synergistic effects is considered in detail in chapter 1, 'Long-Term Risks?', but the impact of behaviour is probably as important as the chemistry of drinking, and the consumer should not expect to find an answer to abuse of alcohol in particular, simply by selecting additive-free drinks – there is more to it than that. Useful techniques of approach include the frank recognition of a drinking lifestyle which, unchecked, may lead to alcohol dependence or alcoholism. The often-quoted (and graphically-illustrated) tragedies of alcoholism should, nevertheless, be viewed in context. First, medical authorities differ on exactly what constitutes alcoholism and, second, most people drink alcohol. Only one in ten people is a true teetotaller, and it may be that some of these do not drink because they are unwell, rather than being made unwell by drinking.

'Name your poison' runs the age-old invitation to join another drinker in raising a glass. The poison of choice is beer, which definition includes ale, lager and stout, with 32 million pints of beer being drunk in Britain every day, confirming it as the world's favourite alcoholic drink. Many of these beer-drinkers also consume wine and spirits, such 'omnibibulous' drinkers being the most at risk from severe hangovers, and long-term risk of brain- and liver-damage, which increases in direct proportion to the amount of times they raise their glasses!

Human beings are the only animals able to absorb alcohol directly through the gullet and stomach wall before it reaches the small intestine. The effects of this substance upon us may therefore be unique, perhaps explaining its addictive power over some people, and possibly explaining the existence of an enzyme in the human liver – alcohol dehydrogenase.

While we may need to consider the physiological risks implicit in the 'gullet' relationship, medical detail is seldom of appeal to the lay person, and attempts to cut hard drugs-use by means of scare-tactics show that these techniques do not work. As with hardened drinkers, bad habits have been too long a part of the subject's lifestyle to alter them through an emotional response.

As with most complex subjects, personal experience is valuable, but only in association with knowledge, the two together forming the basis of judgement. Finding out what goes into drinks of all forms, and learning how they are produced, can provide a good working basis for such value judgements – if the drinker also watches for the signposts to safer drinking.

## Hot on the Trail of the Missing Ingredients

There are two main questions to be answered in the search for healthier drinks and drinking: 'How are drinks produced?' and 'How might a combination of alcohol and other substances in drinks affect the consumer?' I have taken eight main routes towards answering these questions:

(1) a study of the principal ingredients of drinks and their residual substances;
(2) an estimation of the amount and effects of alcohol in drinks;
(3) methods of drinking habit self-inspection and how to 'add up' risk factors;
(4) the inherent nature of the drinks, including production techniques;
(5) examples of additive-free beers and ciders, and organic wines;
(6) a review of common myths and fallacies about drinks and drinking;
(7) the legislative framework within which drinks are produced, including named officials of advisory bodies;
(8) anatomy sketches of the principal additives and their likely effects upon drinkers.

Readers are assisted in finding their way along these 'B' roads, which run parallel with the main questioning routes, by a glossary of terms and substances. By following the general guidelines provided and noting the commercially available 'alternative drinks', a drinker should be able to choose healthier (and less painful!) fluids.

## Oiling the Human Machine

We should keep in mind while looking at the nature of the basic
fluids, that drinking is a strongly social phenomenon, with
subtle implications for business (where it's a lubricant) and for
personal relationships (where it can be anything the drinker
wants it to be).

Alcohol is the only socially acceptable drug, confirmed by the
fact that it is not hunted down and destroyed by the police, as
are most hauls of cannabis (which is related to the hop), cocaine
and heroin. The two latter drugs are highly addictive, as is
tobacco, in all its forms.

It may be significant that the state can control and tax
alcoholic drinks, because most are commercially produced: it
cannot do so as easily with home-grown narcotics such as
cannabis.

We should also keep in mind that at the root of our
endeavours to find out about the nature of drinks, there exists
what appears to be an industry-wide and worldwide charade:
the promotion of the idea that healthy, good-looking drinks can
be produced only by means of highly technical methods and
plant. THIS ASSERTION IS FALSE. Home winemakers and home
brewers do it, cheaply, on the kitchen table! Distilling at home
remains illegal, without a licence.

Because little is likely to change in matters of ingredient-
listing of drinks, my aim in researching and writing about this
subject has been to give drinkers the information they may need
to make cautious choices for years to come. In the unlikely event
that drinks ingredient labelling is introduced, *Name Your Poison!*
will continue to serve as a reference work to techniques and
substances.

Were I to choose a proverb to represent my approach in this
book, perhaps the most appropriate would be: 'He who is
master of his thirst is master of his health,' which clearly has
more significance for women than for men, in view of their
recommended lower intake levels of alcohol (see chapter 2).

Throughout our lives we either act upon or ignore advice
related to many topics, some trivial, some vital, but the closest
most people get to reliable information on balanced drinking
often comes from a slurred source at the bar, from the inaccurate
and sensationalized 'scares' featured in newspapers, or from the

biased blasts of the pro- and anti-alcohol pressure groups. A further source is the wide circle of gossip, which concentrates on who has been 'driven to drink' by whom, or who can't 'hold a drink', but there is much more to today's drinks and drinking than can be obtained via the grapevine.

Drinkers certainly won't be burdened with information overkill from either the producers or the government in Britain, Europe or the USA. This general reticence to inform consumers is regarded by some people as sinister, but I am inclined to attribute it mainly to a combination of studied indifference and bureaucratic inefficiency. It may also be due in part to a tendency apparent in most governments – a greater interest in the health of industrial balance sheets than in the health of consumers and taxpayers.

Where drinks and other foodstuffs are concerned though, I believe that careless attitudes in bodies which should be accountable to parliament and consumers, especially in Britain, could evaporate, and many health-risk factors be eliminated, were a Ministry of Food Safety independent of the MAFF, the Department of Health and the food producers to be set up, on the same lines as the FDA (Food and Drug Administration) in the USA.

By means of specialized agencies this regulation body checks additives, foodstuffs and drugs for toxicity or infection potential independently of the food producers, although it frequently finds itself in headlong conflict with the latter. An example of this conflict occurred in 1988 when the FDA issued a warning about the pesticide Alar (daminozide) which is sprayed on many young apples as they grow, to improve their appearance, and therefore finds its way into apple juice and cider worldwide. The FDA's warning on the cancer-generating potential of the substance met vociferous objections, which continue to reverberate.

It is difficult to imagine such an agency being set up in Britain if official pronouncements are an indication of intent, or rather, the lack of it! In its issue of 22 March 1989 the *Guardian* newspaper reported Baroness Trumpington, then Parliamentary Secretary at the MAFF as blaming supermarkets for 'refusing to take over the cost of food research currently borne by the state, but now being cut' – a majestic example of buck-passing.

While the FDA is often attacked by American consumer

groups as being 'in the pocket of the producers', as are the food control agencies in Britain and Europe, there is, in the USA, some overt control of drinks and drinks-related matters. All matters dealing with labelling, ingredients and additives to alcoholic drinks are dealt with by the BATF (Bureau of Alcohol, Tobacco and Firearms) a department of the Treasury in Washington DC. Other food matters are dealt with by the FDA's Division of Regulatory Guidance in Rockville, Maryland or in Washington DC.

Where BATF is concerned, it seems realistic to attempt to regulate three of the most dangerous human interests (booze, nicotine and bullets) under one roof.

The Food Safety Act 1990, though superseding some clauses of the Food Act 1984 and the Food and Drinks (Scotland) Act 1956, leaves the British labelling regulations and the Food and Drugs Act 1955 untouched. No changes in the 1984 Food Labelling Regulations are suggested. This was predictable in that the use of the word 'safety' in the title of the 1990 Act may indicate the British government's desire to calm public fears about bacterial infection of foodstuffs, following a year of embarrassments for the regulation authorities, and not its resolve to tighten up regulation aspects.

A clause in the 1990 Act makes it an offence to provide false or misleading information on labels, as did the 1984 labelling regulations! Whether this new Act will result in an improvement in labelling enforcement remains to be seen.

The 1990 Act recommends more frequent inspection of food manufacturing and retailing premises. This could only be achieved by recruiting and training more environmental health officers. The main reason inspections of food- and drinks-factories are so infrequent is that, once again, Britain is dependent on 'the few' as it was in 1940.

# 1   Questions of Substance

That is the essence of science; ask an impertinent question and you are on the way to a pertinent answer.

Prof. J. Bronowski, *The Ascent of Man*

## Feeding the Fecund Fungus

Take a bottled drink from any supermarket or off-licence shelf and you can't help but admire the colour and clarity of the contents.

In spite of their apparently pure cosmetic qualities, however, all alcoholic drinks have one vulgar detail in common – their group intimacy with a single-celled fungus organism called yeast.

Wines and spirits are, in their industrially produced forms, subject to wide variations in method, but the basic life chemistry of all alcoholic drinks is initiated by a natural process of growth: the appetite which yeast possesses for sugars. While it feeds on them (ferments), it produces alcohol and carbon dioxide gas as by-products.

In wine and cider the sugar is fruit-derived (from grapes and apples) and is known as fructose; in beer it is barley- or wheat-derived and is known as maltose or dextrose, while spirits are distilled from previously fermented infusions of cereal sugar sources or from cane sugar (rum). There is a great variety of fermenting base materials and a predictably enormous range of mixed concoctions result from their use, but the framework within which British drinks-producers work is controlled (if that is the correct word!) mainly by guidelines laid down in an official report of 1978 entitled *Report on the Review of Additives and Processing Aids used in the Production of Beer*. This report was prepared by the Food Additives and Contaminants Committee (FACC) which has now been absorbed into the Food Advisory Committee (FAC).

The report, which in theory controls the nature and quantity of additives to alcoholic drinks produced in Britain but in practice lays down no basic drinks materials standards, was commissioned by the MAFF.

With the exception of the provisions of the Food and Drugs Act 1955 and the general guidelines of the Food Act 1984*, there are no regulations governing the production of or ingredients used in the manufacture of drinks in Britain. Inspections are not made on a routine basis to check on processes or materials, and the provisions of the controlling legislation are acted upon only as a result of a complaint being received. Strictly speaking, somebody must be poisoned by a product before any action is taken – in arrears, as is usual under the law. In other countries this 'after the event' control has resulted in deaths from adulterated beer and wine.

A clause in the Food Labelling Regulations 1984 excludes from the Act all drinks with an alcohol content exceeding 1.2 per cent by volume (ABV). This means that only low and non alcoholic wines, ciders and beers must be so labelled. Why the regulations promote such an inverted approach to alcohol (surely the priority should be to list the strength of stronger, rather than weaker drinks?) has never been explained, although it may well be on public view somewhere at the bottom of a 500-foot cliff, locked in a steel safe, inside which is a bureaucrat's CONFIDENTIAL file carrying the warning 'Beware of cyanide gas'.

Since drinkers are the geese which lay the golden revenue egg (see below), there seems no good reason why successive Chancellors of the Exchequer should permit them to be poisoned. It all seems very odd until you consider the vast revenue governments extract, providing no services in return, from alcoholic drinks.

In Britain, for example, revenue from beer (the most popular drink) for the year 1988/89 amounted to £2,100 millions, excluding VAT, which accounted for a further £1,000 million. This represented a four per cent increase on the previous year.

The total for all alcoholic drinks in Britain amounted to £4,447 million in Excise Duty and £2,355 million as VAT, according to a Treasury statement (Hansard, June 1988), a 2.3 per cent increase on the previous year.

* The Beer Regulations 1988 deal with revenue aspects and not with brewing practice, additives or ingredients.

The dissemination of detailed information on possible residual dangers in drinks COULD CUT THESE TOTALS, which are set to rise considerably in the 1990s, due to an expected rise in consumption of alcohol. This rise is likely to result from two factors:

(1) alcoholic drinks are becoming cheaper in real terms, because drinks prices have not kept pace with wage increases in the past five years;

(2) all-day opening of licensed premises.

It is therefore important for drinkers to know more about drinks. Had the residual ingredients of the fluids they drink been established as safe, and evidence presented to the public, perhaps not knowing how much alcohol is about to be consumed in each glass might not loom large as a problem, but what about the possible risks of alcohol and additives taken together? The dubious composition of some drinks makes the search for such information essential for the intelligent drinker.

Purity, however, is not something that can be judged simply by appearances. When you hold a pint of real ale up to the light just after Tiny Tim, the sixteen-stone cellarman, has nudged the cask down below with his ten-pound hammer, the cloudy lumps you see swirling around are much the least dangerous of additives – just a few bits of fish buoyancy bladders (see Finings – Glossary).

## Limits or Licence?

In a survey I conducted with the aim of establishing the extent to which materials other than traditional ingredients are used in the British drinks industry, several of the larger concerns refused to give details but added that their use of additives is 'within legal and health limits'.

They certainly can't know what the long-term effects upon drinkers might be, because their laboratories are not concerned with such matters, and except for Imperial Cancer Research Fund enquiries, there is no general investigation of such dangers.

But just what are the legal constraints?

As we have seen, the Food Act of 1955 prohibits the addition to food of any injurious substances, and this same Act also lays down general provisions and regulations which are concerned with constituents of foodstuffs.

It is no accident that the Food Additives and Contaminants Committee was so named. Its original function was to consider additives and contaminants in foodstuffs, in relation to their possible harmful effects upon consumers. Perhaps the committee's absorption into the FAC in 1983 came as a result of the 'bad press' additives were getting at the time. Terms such as 'advisory' are more positive than 'contaminants'.

No doubt the time will come when the relevant committee will be provided with an even softer image in its title (hoping not to offend the genteel person) and be called 'The Committee to watch over Cuddly Fluffy Bunnies and Guinea Pigs in the Laboratories'.

The clubbing to death of baby seals in the Arctic may grab more media attention and trigger more public outrage, but this cruelty exists on a small scale compared with the millions of animals of several species which die in toxicity tests worldwide. Professor Peter Singer estimated that more than five million such animals would die in British laboratories during 1977. Figures are now more difficult to obtain (perhaps because of the publication of *Animal Liberation* by Peter Singer!), but they are thought likely to be increasing.

Still in widespread use is the so-called L.D. 50 test for toxicity, using as test subjects monkeys, dogs, baboons, rabbits, guinea pigs, rats and mice. The initials L.D. stand for 'lethal dosage', the name of the test which monitors the amount of toxin (i.e. component of a medicine, drug or food additive) used in the test, which will kill 50 per cent of the animals tested. The demise of each individual animal is unceremoniously marked by TDA (technician destroyed animal) in the laboratory log.

Only a quarter of such tests are considered sufficiently valid to warrant publication and most are of doubtful relevance to human health. Animals are cared for and stroked until the final day, in order not to distort the test's results by generating fear-induced toxins in their blood.

## Regulations and Limits

There are no specific regulations dealing with the composition or labelling of drinks (except low or non-alcoholic forms) but the Arsenic in Food Regulations 1959 (amended in 1960 and 1973) prescribe maxima of 0.55 ppm (parts per million) in black beer –

a herbal product – and 0.2 ppm in other alcoholic beverages. The Lead in Food Regulations 1961 (amended in 1973 and 1975) prescribe an upper limit of 0.55 ppm. The Preservatives in Food Regulations 1975 (amended in 1976 and 1979) lay down maximum levels of the following substances:

IN BEER AND CIDER:
70 mg of each of the following preservatives in each kg of the drink – *benzoic acid*, or *ethyl 4-hydroxybenzoate*, or *propyl para-hydroxybenzoate*, or *methyl 4-hydroxybenzoate* or *sulphur dioxide*, or their permitted alternative forms, a total of seventeen additives.

IN WINE:
*potassium sorbate* (maximum 200 mg per litre), or *sulphur dioxide* (maximum of 0.7 mg per every 1 kg of the drinker's body weight), or *sodium sulphite* (same levels), or *sodium hydrogen sulphite* (same levels) or *sodium metabisulphite* (same levels), or *potassium metabisulphite* (same levels).

How a drinks-manufacturer is expected to estimate the body weight of each potential drinker before these preservatives are added to drinks is not clear!

Several other MAFF surveillance papers deal with lead and arsenic in general foodstuffs (see bibliography)

IN SPIRITS AND LIQUEURS:
none specified.

For the report produced by the FACC in 1978, twenty-six organizations, including BDH Chemicals, Colin Stewart Minerals, Alginate Industries Ltd and BP Chemicals, made representations or provided data to the committee. Between them, these organizations submitted more than sixty-eight substances for consideration.

Of these, some of which are enzymes and others derivatives of a 'parent' material (e.g. sulphur dioxide and its six variant forms), fifty-nine remain in the drink supplied to the customer.

More than sixty of the original sixty-eight submitted to the committee for approval were placed in its Group A – 'Substances that the available evidence suggests are suitable for food use'. These substances were therefore approved for continued use in brewing.

## Profit on Tap

Ask a drinks-manufacturer to describe his best-selling item and you are likely to be told that it's a 'healthy and sophisticated product which is very popular with the drinker'.

It's probably even more popular with the local water company, because the greater part of most drinks consists of Adam's Ale, or Adam's Wine, both of which are ancient names for water.

Whether your favourite drink is wine, lager, ale, cider, perry or a cola drink, most of what goes down the hatch emerged from somebody's tap or was pumped up from a well, so most of the producer's 'sophistication' applies to the jiggery-pokery which goes on in the drinks factories and is concerned mainly with substances other than water. The main ingredient of your drink has therefore already been paid for in terms of its rateable value, making it a very highly profitable ingredient indeed.

The exceptions to the 'mainly water' rule are spirits such as over-proof rum and vodka, which may exceed seventy per cent by volume, but the mark-up on the base fluid (water) is quite as good for the distiller as for the winemaker and brewer.

With the acceptance by the British government of an EEC directive to take effect in July 1989, making it legally binding on producers to indicate a drink's alcohol content on the container (cask, keg, can or bottle) we should be able to assess the amount of water in each drink by a simple process of subtraction. For example, allowing for the four per cent of a glass of whisky which consists of solids, the remaining 56 per cent of a forty per cent by volume example consists of water.

The residents of Camelford, Cornwall, may hold a unique view on the matter. In the summer of 1988 water supplies to the town were contaminated by an over-use of aluminium sulphate, which is used by some water companies as finings (clarifying agents) of cloudy water. It is thought that the incident may have posed an increased risk to drinkers of the water of developing Altzheimer's disease (a form of senile dementia) later in life, due to the increased intake of aluminium. This intake may be increased where the drinker consumes drinks clarified with bentonite (see Appendix 2), or cooks with aluminium saucepans. Where beer and cider are concerned, more than ninety per cent of the drink consists of water, and at least eighty-five per cent of wine.

So now we have a further probable reason why drinks-producers continue to resist calls for ingredient-labelling of alcoholic drinks. Labelling requirements insist that the largest ingredient be labelled first – 'water' sounds none too impressive as the principal ingredient of your 'sophisticated' ale, lager or cider, especially if you hope to sell it at around £1.50 per pint, disregarding for the moment the fact that alcoholic drinks are now very cheap when compared with wage rates.

Similarly, a good bottle of wine costing about £12 would hardly benefit commercially from the revelation on the art-worked fancy label showing the Comte du Nord's fairy-tale *château* that eighty-four per cent of the contents may have been piped in from the moat!

The productive people who sit at their typewriters inventing new reasons why Old Crow's Foot Brandy is good for 101 holiday delights are hundreds of years behind the experts in the trade, when it comes to crafty copy on the subject. In the seventeenth century (some sources say earlier) brewers took a definitive step in fudging the image of their product when they decided to call the water used in brewing 'liquor', which definition continues in the industry today. They certainly knew the value of a good euphemism!

The sly move did not fool the Weights and Measures people, however, who kept an even closer eye on brewers, albeit with little effect. For the five years of the Second World War, beer of all forms was in short supply in Britain, due to shortages of malt. Although malt was imported from California, USA, in response to the Ministry of Agriculture's zippy slogan 'Get some sun into your mash tun', this had little effect because most of it was of poor quality, yielding a low extraction rate. In 1943 almost one-third of licensees in the London area were thought to be adding more 'liquor' to their ales and stouts, in order to maintain volume sales (as it were!), but only a handful were convicted during the war years.

When a licensee with the highly appropriate name of John Waters was fined for the offence in Brighton in 1981, the penalty had still not been updated, pound for pound.

Watering of cask beers continues even today, with very few offenders being prosecuted or convicted for what is, after all, unmitigated theft. If your daily pint of bitter or mild reveals an unusual softness to the palate (less bitter bitter, less malty mild), the chances are that you are paying for more water than is permitted – up to twenty per cent of the drink may have been lost, which would probably delight the people at Alcohol Concern! Tests show that most drinkers cannot detect the fact when up to one-fifth of a beer has been extracted and water substituted. Brewers can check for watering of cask beers by a colour test of the fluid.

## What Else Is In It for the Drinker?

The quantity of additives and processing aids which remain in beer especially may be surprising, but exactly why are these non-traditional ingredients used?

In *Brewing Review* (the journal of the Brewers' Society) for February 1987 an unidentified writer explains: 'Additives and processing aids are used in brewing to increase the performance of the natural raw materials. They are not in any way substitutes for malt, hops or yeast or any other basic ingredient.' The only 'basic ingredient' not mentioned by the invisible man is water, which is certainly modified as much as any other. Minerals are added, as are various yeast foods and enzyme preparations, all of which increase yields and consequent profit. It is in this way that additives are used to boost the performance of the raw materials – commercially, once again, and not for sound brewing or health reasons. The thing they boost most is profit.

Since tap water contains a fair amount of minerals, as do 'natural mineral waters' in bottles (at a fancy price!), there seems no good reason to add more, unless they confer a commercial benefit. The truth is that each form of water is marketed to its highest profit point, or fiddled, to make it profitable. It seems reasonable to conclude, though, that drinks-promoters have missed their chance to launch Sellafield (Windscale) Mineral Water as a 'sophisticated product'!

The quantity and range of brewing and winemaking additives can be observed by visiting a home-brew supplies shop. These shops receive 'domestic' quantities of materials used in large-scale brewing as they are developed in the brewers' laboratories. A single visit to such a shop is sufficient to confirm that everything needed to brew impure wine or beer is there, from a bewildering array of different acids and yeast foods (unnecessary to a properly formulated wort or must) to fining (clarifying) agents and enzyme preparations.

Curiously, most of these shops, and the home-brew industry

generally, depend upon a 'good, natural beer and wine' theme as the basis of their business.

The 'health food' angle is not a new phenomenon, however, and the sometimes mystical nature of secret medicines and specifics (cure-alls) was matched in Victorian times by a movement towards what we might now describe as 'green' drinks, with ingredients drawn from the hedgerows.

As the twentieth century opened, drinkers were offered numerous routes to good health by dozens of make-believe doctors. One of the well-packaged concoctions which found its way into thirsty but health-conscious drinkers was Dr Watson's Tonic Stout (see p.197) which may or may not have depended for its immediately identifiable image on the then best-selling fictional companion of Sherlock Holmes. The drink was certainly not elementary and contained, said the good 'doctor', 'malt, hops, kola nut, dandelion and co.' Alcohol was not mentioned! Its tonic elements clearly included a few hedgerow additives (dandelion is a diuretic, not a stimulant), but at least its creator was prepared to tell drinkers most of what his stout contained, unlike his modern industrial counterpart. Kola nut extracts are constituents, with sulphite ammonia caramel and aspartame or benzoic acid, of most cola-type carbonated soft drinks. Such extracts contain caffeine and other stimulant alkaloids. A postcard carrying the original advertising artwork for Dr Watson's, can be seen in the Robert Opie Collection, Gloucester.

Going back even farther, a substance called quassia (not to be confused with quillaia, the natural heading-agent) was often added to ale in the mid-eighteenth century, replacing the bittering effect of hops, which were expensive. As well as this tree resin from South America, copperas (green vitriol), a copper salt of iron, was sometimes mixed with alum to create a thick head of foam on ale in the glass. It was said to produce a head which 'resembled a colliflower' but could hardly have been recommended for drinkers other than those with an iron constitution.

In *Cottage Economy*, published in 1822, William Cobbett, the Radical MP and founder of *The Political Register* (now *Hansard*), denounced 'beer druggists and ale doctors'. He followed up his denunciation with an outline of typical ingredients for one of their so-called 'ales': 'Take one quarter of high coloured malt, eight pounds of hops, nine pounds of treacle, eight pounds of colour, eight pounds of sliced licorice root, two drams of salt of tartar, two ounces of Spanish licorice and half an ounce of capsicum.' It must have tasted more like ratatouille than beer!

Brewers now have a better understanding of the meaning of the term 'toxic', and laboratory routines conducted by the BIBRA (British Industrial Biological Research Association) can identify problems of short-term (acute) toxicity.

Another area of the subject where particularly close scrutiny works in favour of the drinker's health is in the work of the maltsters, both those working within the breweries and those within the specialist malting concerns, such as Paul's Malt of Ipswich and Munton & Fison of Stowmarket. The main concern of such specialists is the control of nitrosamines, potential carcinogens (cancer-forming substances), which can be generated in the barley during kilning.

Oxides of nitrogen, known as '$NO_x$' (pronounced 'knocks') in the industry, which are already present in the barley, resulting either from organic changes in the soil or from nitrate residues of fertilizers, act upon dimethylamine (a carcinogen) also present in the grain, to produce these harmful substances. They can, however, be virtually eliminated by the modern process of indirect kilning, which employs very hot air rather than direct heating in the presence of sulphur, which was the traditional method.

Formerly, acidic additives such as phosphoric acid were also used to limit nitrosamines, but the industry has taken its own initiative in converting to safer techniques, aiming to eliminate any risk to drinkers. Maltsters consider that their product, which has many uses in confectionery as well as in distilling and malted drinks, is less harmful than many other foodstuffs. One example is bacon, which is invariably treated with E250 sodium nitrite, a potentially hazardous preservative which, it must be said, is essential in order to protect its consumers against infection by Clostridium botulinum, the organism which produces botulism.

Nitrites are synthetically or biologically generated and may also cause nitrosamines to form in the stomach, and they exist in relatively large amounts in bacon, compared with the minute amounts of nitrate and nitrosamines which exist in well-kilned malt. One maltster expressed the opinion that the 'scare' about beers being dangerously packed with nitrosamines was 'a further indication that the anti-alcohol lobby are desperate to emphasize details out of context, even when they are so clearly based upon faulty analysis and general misreporting'.

Further, since nitrosamines are volatile, they are given off when the malt mixture is boiled with hops, making the resulting beer safer, in terms of this specific risk, than bacon and other cooked, processed meats and processed fish.

## Long-term Risks?

The services of the specialist maltsters function to the benefit of the drinker, but countering this factor is the 'negative study' effect. That is, long-term observation of drinkers is not undertaken, and little work has been done on the possible effects of the two main additives to beer, for example: E150(c) ammonia caramel and E405 propylene glycol alginate, which are added to most keg ales and many real ales. Ammonia caramel is also added to red wine to improve (redden) its colour, and in brewing this and other synthetic colouring matters are gradually replacing the traditional malt grains, such as crystal (light brown), amber (golden) and black malt or 'chocolate' malt.

E405 is a widely used ester of alginic acid, employed as a head-retaining agent in all keg ales and lagers, many real ales and most bottled and canned beers. It is known as Manucol Ester 'B' in the USA.

Where the caramel colours are concerned, there are three other main forms:

E150 sulphite ammonia caramel, which is used mainly to give extra colour to cola-type soft drinks and vinegar;

E150(a) plain spirit caramel, which is thought to pose no risks to drinkers, but is little-used by producers;

E150(b) caustic sulphite caramel, which is used mainly to colour whisky and brandy.

In 1984 caramel colours accounted for ninety-eight per cent of all colouring matter added to food in Britain, but figures are not available for the quantities used in drinks.

When a prospective drinker reads the term 'caramel' or 'colour' on, for example, a bottle of ginger ale, there is no way of knowing which caramel has been used in the drink. The Food Labelling Regulations permit producers to describe additives either by a description of their function in the food (colouring matter', 'antioxidant', etc.), by E number alone, or by their chemical names. Confusion rules and the drinker little wiser about the nature of the additive.

The main worry now is concerned not so much with the immediate toxic effects of additives (or alcohol) in drinks as with the cumulative effects over several years, and especially over many years for regular moderate drinkers, bearing in mind that alcohol is itself a carcinogen.

While two substances taken separately, or at intervals, may be safe, when they are combined they may pose a risk. Enzyme activity in the human cell is of significance in this respect.

In the course of a seminar I attended at Surrey University in 1988, which was concerned partly with the use of laboratory animals for toxicity testing ('animal assay'), some of the latest findings of cytology, the science of the study of cells, were outlined. Professor Denis Parke pointed to reactions initiated by cytochromes (iron-bearing enzymes in human and animal cells) reacting with introduced substances (i.e. those eaten by the individual), such reactions being possible cancer-triggers.

In *The Causes of Cancer*, Sir Richard Doll and Richard Peto, commenting on the use of laboratory animals as human 'surrogates' for the testing of toxicity, say, considering the artificial sweetener saccharin, which is often combined with aspartame in soft drinks or cola drinks: 'Human exposure to a weak carcinogen may need to be prolonged for several decades before any positive effect can be detected, and no assurances can be given that an effect will not be produced by a lifetime of exposure to the unusually large amounts that are consumed in diet drinks by some children and young adults.'

In *Diet, Nutrition and Cancer*, a report by the American National Academy of Sciences, the possibility of two or more substances (i.e. additives) reacting and producing an undesirable effect not shown in tests on rats of the substances singly, is mooted: 'The possibility that they may act synergistically and may therefore create a greater carcinogenic risk cannot be excluded.'

Consider all these points in relation to the numerous good-looking fluids which find their way into bottles, cans, casks and kegs all over Britain, Europe and the USA. With the exception of those which are produced by the small or independent British brewers who use no additives, and by organic winemakers, these drinks are the result of the application of a sophisticated blend of laboratory skills and marketing expertise on basic alcoholic beverages, using many ingredients and additives.

Should the big producer comment that, 'The customer prefers a good-looking drink', there is still no need to employ preservatives. Many of the small drinks concerns which have started production in the past fifteen years (there are 150 small breweries and 200 wineries in Britain) use no preservatives, although some use filtering-aids, and most concentrate upon building flavour into their products rather than long life.

In contrast, preservatives, typically those of the sulphur dioxide 'group', are present in most commercially produced ciders from the large combines and certainly in all the beers they brew. They are there mainly to extend the saleability of the drinks and have little to do with 'preventing human disease' or 'promoting stability', as one brewing giant's press releases explain.

I believe that when E220 sulphur dioxide (or one of its variant forms) is present in a drink which is mixed with a drink or drinks containing E210 benzoic acid, they can produce a 'double-up' effect in terms of the eventual hangover. Labelling of drinks to show ingredients would prevent many of these reactions (if the reader acted upon the information!). Alcohol content details similarly help to reduce 'treble-up' effects. E210 and E220 are probably the two most reactive additives used in drinks.

As yet, there is no evidence to suggest that any of the permitted additives to drinks is acutely toxic, in the amounts to be found in most examples, but as biologist Dr R.D. Combes points out in his *Introduction to the Safety Assessment (Toxicity) of Additives*:

In addition to effects occurring rapidly (short-term, acute or sub-acute effects) such as poisoning, chemicals can exert changes which arise some considerable time after exposure (chronic effects). The latter can occur later on in the same generation (e.g. cancer) or in later generations as birth defects and inherited diseases, the consequences of which may not become apparent for several hundred years. This is because they are due to alterations that may not be reflected immediately in that chemical (the genetic material DNA) which is present in all the chromosomes in all the body cells and which determines all our characteristics. Chronic effects are often due to *continuous exposure to small amounts of chemical over long periods of time*, a situation which occurs when we eat food and from any constituents of the food. Unfortunately, most people seem to be more concerned about the immediate consequences of chemicals where the link between exposure and side-effects is more obvious.

## Deadly Drinks

An example of the dangers of regular exposure to additives in drinks, and one where both short- and long-term effects might have been noted, had action not been taken, was the Austrian wine scandal of 1984, when possibly lethal quantities of diethylene glycol, a substance which sometimes forms a component of motor-vehicle anti-freeze, were added to wine to give it 'body'.

The adulteration of the wine came to light only because a wary VAT inspector noted the wine-producer's claim for reimbursement of the cost of what appeared to be a large quantity of an unfamiliar material.

A bottle of this wine tested in the north of England proved to contain 1.5 ml of the contaminant; the ingestion of 0.3 ml of this substance per day is considered highly dangerous, and 100 ml can be fatal. In spite of the potential seriousness of this incident, it is amusing to contemplate the unpopular VAT man as the hero of the piece!

It is thought that many drinkers in imperial Rome may have died prematurely as a result of drinking wine contaminated with lead, which found its way into the wine from the lead-lined pots used to hold the raw grape juice.

Incredible though it may seem, armed as they were with hindsight about such dangers, the Victorians sometimes added lead to acidic wines in order to soften their effect upon the palate!

In addition to the modern Austrian 'antifreeze' incident, several Americans and Canadians died in the early 1960s after drinking beer which had been adulterated with cobalt sulphate. The substance had been added as an alternative to E405 propylene glycol alginate, the head-retaining agent. People therefore lost their lives in the interests of a drink-producer's desire to maintain cosmetic standards in beer.

In China in 1985 three men were executed for manufacturing a version of rice wine which had been 'fortified' with methyl alcohol, the highly poisonous form.

In a sense, you may be taking your life in your hands by drinking any wine which has no ingredients pedigree. Following the reverberations of the Austrian wine scandal of 1984, during which the chief investigating police officer committed suicide, public interest has dropped back into its usual half-an-ear cocked position, which is potentially risky for any drinker.

More recently, a scandal similar to the Austrian affair erupted in Japan, although the alleged contaminated wine 'disappeared', due to an employee's 'oversight'.

Italy had its own wine scandal in 1986, when twenty-two Italians died after drinking wine which had been laced with methyl alcohol. Once again, the lethal wine 'disappeared' before people could be brought to book.

The truth is that a drinker really has no way of knowing how a wine has been produced, and producers are hardly likely to reveal the fact if it has been chemically fiddled. Your taste-buds won't tell you these details, and you will have to fight against the well-developed image of wine, even within your own consciousness to some extent, which persists in saying, 'They couldn't do that to Chäteau Neasden, could they?'

Nicholas Tomalin, who was killed while reporting the Yom Kippur War of 1973, revealed in a British Sunday newspaper the practice of wine-shippers who offered customers in the trade any labels they wanted, to stick to the wine bottles, all filled from the same enormous tanker ship!

However, some beer-producers are prepared to throw open their breweries to the public, so their products are virtually guaranteed.

It could be argued that, even were there stringent ingredient labelling requirements for alcoholic drinks, dangerous acts of crass commercialism would not necessarily be avoided.

Nevertheless, a wide range of additives is employed in the production of all alcoholic drinks manufactured on a large scale. Their physical effects upon drinkers are perhaps a little more subtle than those of diethylene glycol and certainly less immediate, but were labelling to be employed, at least people who are said to suffer most from ingesting substances such as benzoic acid or sulphur dioxide (e.g. some asthmatics and nettle-rash [urticaria] sufferers) would be able to avoid drinks which they knew contained them.

## The Risk from Urethane and Lead

One of the most worrying constituents of alcoholic drinks is a substance called urethane, also known as ethyl carbamate or carbamic acid ethyl ester.

Very little information has been disseminated in Britain and Europe about this potent carcinogen, but in the USA groups such as the CSPI (Center for Science in the Public Interest) and the FDA have been trying to establish guidelines for acceptable levels of the chemical, which was recognized as an animal carcinogen in 1943.

Until it was banned by the FDA in 1972, an additive to drinks, DEPC (diethyl pyrocarbonate) was found to react with their natural ingredients to form urethane. However, urethane is generated by the normal process of fermentation or distillation, and ageing (maturing) of whiskies and wines, for example, may increase its concentration. Beer appears to be relatively safe, but urethane is present in very small quantities in most alcoholic drinks.

Unlike most carcinogens, however, small amounts of urethane can pose a danger, and cancers could be produced in the lungs, mammary glands (breasts), liver, skin, lymphatic system and gastro-intestinal tract of drinkers.

Following the banning of the use of DEPC, a Canadian laboratory technician started to note urethane in spirit drinks and wines made without the additive. Moves behind the scenes by the big producers kept the regulation authorities in the dark until a group of Canadian scientists developed spectrographic analytical methods for identifying amounts of the substance down to a few parts per billion (ppb).

Following up these advances, the FDA and BATF in the USA began checking drinks products for urethane levels, testing about a thousand drinks up to the time of writing.

In the summer of 1989 Dr Gary Flamm, the FDA's chief food toxicologist, writing in the *Philadelphia Inquirer*, said: 'Urethane is a carcinogen that should be feared. Ranking substances by the threat they pose to cause cancer in humans, urethane would be first, second or third.'

While there is no 'safe' level of any carcinogen (bodily risk factors will vary as widely as those posed by alcohol alone), the CSPI has estimated from studies based upon testing with rats and mice that 4,700 people in every million who drink moderate amounts of urethane-contaminated drinks may contract cancer. This level, they estimate, could be as low as that consumed in three daily glasses of bourbon at 150 ppb or wine containing 30 ppb urethane.

The drinking of some table wines may parallel Russian roulette, in that, although some contain no urethane, others have revealed 270 ppb, nine times the maximum level suggested in Canada, where the most stringent checks are carried out. Canadian limits are: table wine 30 ppb, fortified wines 100 ppb, spirits 150 ppb, fruit brandies 400 ppb.

In general, distilled drinks or liqueurs such as European fruit brandies contain the highest amounts of urethane, followed by bourbon, cream sherries, port wines, Japanese saké and Chinese wines such as rice wine.

In its own listing of tested drinks, entitled *Tainted Booze*, the CSPI published (1987) data on urethane levels in numerous brands. Those with the highest levels head the list:

|  |  | urethane in ppb |
|---|---|---|
| Czechoslovakia | Jelinek Slivovitz (plum brandy) | 1,633–2,454 |
| The Netherlands | Bols Kirschwasser (cherry brandy) | 1,497–7,194 |
| France | Jacquins Kirschwasser (cherry brandy) | 2,078 |
| Yugoslavia | Manastirka Slivovitz (plum brandy) | 1,256–2,009 |

In a more comprehensive list, the CSPI gives details of numerous American-made bourbons and whiskies and world-made wines, with significantly high urethane levels, including Jack Daniel's Old No.7 (178 ppb), Jim Beam's Choice old No.8 (406 ppb), the Swiss fruit brandy Dettling Kirschwasser (1030 ppb), the French Chat Les Justices Sauternes 1983 (32 ppb) and the American Paul Masson Rare Premium California Burgundy (35 ppb).

Other drinks given special mention are Paul Masson Golden

Cream California Sherry (120 ppb), the Japanese Chiyoda Saké (837 ppb) and Ficklin Vineyards California Port (254 ppb). Only one Spanish wine is mentioned – La Rioja Alta Reserva 904 (1970) at 43 ppb, while a French red wine, Maison Ginestet Médoc, is noted at a level of 44 ppb.

In terms of beer, only one is mentioned as having a relatively high level of urethane: the Australian-brewed version of Foster's lager (presumably in canned form) at 11 ppb (no Canadian limit set for beer).

In spite of its continuing effort to inform the drinker about urethane, the CSPI has noted that, although both the *New York Times* and *Washington Post* covered the subject as a health topic, their wine-appreciation columns remain unaffected by it, still with no indication of urethane levels in recommended wines.

Towards the end of her book *The Demon Drink*, Jancis Robinson refers to the 'wildly overblown scare about traces of the carcinogen urethane sniffed out in some wines'. To commit to this important substance only two lines of a 226-page book which purports to deal with alcohol in depth, is inconsistent with the claim printed in its frontispiece – that it is a 'balanced guide' (a quote by *Wine*).

Maybe she should have sniffed a few of the nose-wrinkling European fruit brandies.

Further information on listings of urethane content is available from the Center for Science in the Public Interest, 1501 16th Street, NW Washington DC 20036, USA. Telephone 0101 202 332 9110.

The centre's equivalent organization in Britain is the London Food Commission, 88 Old Street, London EC1V 9AR. Telephone 01 253 9513 (071 253 9513 from 6 May 1990).

## Lead

Water supply pipes made of lead remain the major source of this metal in beer, followed by copper brewery vessels (tuns). These vessels were constructed by soldering together copper sections. Solder is an alloy of lead and tin.

Levels in beer are diminishing as the EEC's guidelines on conversion to stainless steel tuns and dispenser taps take effect. Handpump (real ale) dispensers have been made from brass for many years. Brass is an alloy of several base metals: copper, tin, zinc and sometimes lead.

# 2 Our Beloved Drug

An alcoholic is someone who drinks more than his doctor.
Attributed to Richard Burton, the actor

## The Demon in the Drink

Alcohol, the ingredient in drinks with 'kick', developed its colloquial identity during biblical times. '*Koh'l*' is the Arabic word for antimony sulphide, which was used by women in the Middle East as eye make-up. During the sixteenth-century, the definite article *al* was placed before *koh'l*, creating 'alcohol'. By that time its meaning had become broader, to include any fine powder, especially one derived by vaporizing a solid and then allowing the vapour to condense.

Eventually, in the eighteenth century, 'alcohol of wine' gradually became called simply 'alcohol', and in modern times it is taken to mean any compound consisting of a hydrocarbon group joined to a hydroxyl group of substances.

Most of the alcohol found in drinks is ethyl alcohol (ethanol), although some beverages contain traces of methyl alcohol (methanol), which is often used as a cheap antifreeze medium in car cooling systems. Methyl alcohol is also known as 'wood spirit' or 'wood alcohol', but whatever name it appears under it is considerably the more poisonous of the two forms.

Distillation produces alcohol in its pure, or near-pure, state, and in this form it appears with flavourings and colours in spirit drinks such as whisky and brandy. Fermentation produces alcohol in its very impure state; one of the by-products of fermentation is formaldehyde, a possible carcinogen, but quantities produced in this way are small.

Methylated spirit is industrially produced ethyl alcohol to which has been added some wood spirit (about ten per cent of the volume), a little paraffin oil and a quantity of aniline dye.

Meths-drinkers – or 'winoes' as they are called – can be seen in many industrial town-centre gardens in Britain, drinking from cider bottles. They drink a mixture of meths, wine and cider, and they have perhaps missed the vital information that the purpose of adulterating alcohol with industrial pollutants is to prevent the deadly fluid from being drunk.

Many of these meths-drinkers develop chronic neuritis, and others go blind – some die as a result of mixing meths with rum or vodka.

Modern practice in the brewing and winemaking industries, as in the distilling industry, is to indicate alcoholic strength as a percentage of the volume of the fluid in the final container, i.e., ABV.

The British labelling regulations of 1984 refer to beer 'when sold prepacked', meaning that these bottled and canned forms were excluded from the need to show alcohol-content levels. These requirements were amended by regulations which came into force on 17 July 1989 – the Food Labelling (Amendment) Regulations, which require drinks-producers to list the alcoholic strength of each canned or bottled drink of more than 1.2 per cent ABV on its container.

'Dispensed' full-strength alcoholic drinks (draught forms of wine, beer, cider or perry) must have the alcohol-content of a representative sample shown on a notice, such as a menu or bar tariff. Cocktails and other mixed drinks, such as shandy, are excluded from the latter listing regulations.

These new controls were introduced following another period of derogation by the British government, eventually implementing EEC Council Directives of May 1986 and April 1987. A voluntary code of practice introduced by the Brewers' Society (which represents two-thirds of the industry in Britain) meant that for many years most draught beers have shown an original gravity (og) figure on a clip-on label attached to their dispensers, where they could be clearly seen by the drinker. Many canned and bottled beers have shown either og or the relevant ABV figure, or both. Only ABV is now compulsory, but it is not illegal to indicate og as well.

Indicated alcohol-levels are permitted certain tolerances: beers of less than 5.5 per cent ABV may vary by 0.5 per cent, plus or minus; those above 5.5 per cent ABV are permitted one per cent variation either way, as are bottled or canned ciders and drinks made from honey, such as mead. Draught ciders are permitted 1.5 per cent leeway, and all other alcoholic drinks 0.3 per cent.

In spite of these changes, most long drinks will remain without either an og or ABV marking at a genuinely drinker-accessible point at the bar. In addition, some brewers are likely to convert to ABV markings on handpump clips, because to maintain og markings would tend to act as a marketing disadvantage, since they would appear to be outdated. Within a few years, therefore, og markings (normally quoted as a range or 'band') could disappear from handpumps and casks, not always to be replaced by ABV markings. Should this occur, the new regulations, introduced ostensibly in order to provide more information, will result in less of this rare commodity (in foods matters) being available to the consumer of long drinks.

In a straw poll I conducted in Surrey, Hampshire, Dorset and Cornwall, six weeks after the new regulations became law, out of fifty licensees questioned only two had heard of the Food Labelling Regulations 1984, none was familiar with the amended regulations of 1989, and only six had ever been visited by licensing or trading standards officials. All fifty licensees said they doubted that legal action would be taken should they ignore the regulations.

The (dismissed by bureaucrats) method of og indication, though more difficult to comprehend than ABV, will continue in use by brewers and winemakers worldwide, so an outline of its main principles can aid a better understanding of the variable fermenting chemistry of the different drinks, as well as their respective revenue matters.

Original gravity 'bands' can seem dauntingly over-technical, even mysterious. Although it is by no means true that they have been universally used, some small brewers of real ales are likely to continue to indicate og at the handpump which delivers the beer from the cellar. The indicated range is likely to be 1,032–1,042 for most best bitters, and 1,044–1,058 for most strong ales and strong stouts, such as porter. Very strong ales, sometimes called 'winter warmers' because they are brewed mainly during the winter quarter, may exceed 1,080–1,090 (approximately 9.5–11 per cent by volume) but such high-strength beers are now rare.

The original gravity figure, which is applied generally to beer (and wine in its pre-bottling stage) and not to other beverages, is arrived at by comparing the specific gravity of the wort (the beer before it is fermented) or the must (the wine before it is fermented) with the specific gravity of water, which is taken as 1,000. The resultant figure gives a fairly accurate rule of thumb for deciding the likely alcohol-content of the finished beer or wine, based upon an inferred estimate of the amount of fermentable material the wort or must contains.

This material is likely to be a blend of maltose, dextrose and sucrose from various sources in the case of beer, and grape juice or other fruit and berry juice in the case of wine. Wine original gravities are likely to be in the range 1,095–1,102. Such specific gravity checks do not provide a precise method of alcohol content assessment – the true concentration of alcohol in terms of weight or volume can be checked for an absolute reading only by laboratory means – but og listing gives a good working (or drinking!) indication of the possible effects upon the drinker's brain and liver.

Og is checked by dunking a calibrated float, which brewers and winemakers call a saccharometer (i.e. sugar-content analyser) but which is technically a hydrometer, into the wort or must before fermentation, while final gravity is checked at the end of fermentation.

Tax is levied by a government's excise department (the term 'excise' means 'to cut off or out') based upon these readings, because alcohol is the taxable portion of an alcoholic drink. In Britain this technique was introduced by Gladstone's Brewing Act of 1880, but it had already been roundly condemned (as a principle) by Samuel Johnson two centuries earlier: 'A hateful tax levied upon commodities and adjudged not by the common judges of property, but wretches hired by those to whom excise is paid.'

In the USA, original gravity is employed within breweries, but ABV is marked on containers, as in most of Europe. In Germany, a slightly modified og scale, termed 'degrees Plato', is employed by some brewers, while in Britain a few brewers still use 'brewers' pounds' to assess likely strength. This involves weighing a beer wort before and after fermentation and comparing the result with the weight of the same volume of water.

Original gravity figures may appear in other forms, the range 1,034–1,046, for example, appearing as .34–.46, but the measurement is identical. Because the specific gravity of fluids is affected by temperature, the check is made at 16°C (60°F), which is virtually an ideal temperature at which to introduce the yeast at the start of brewing.

The final gravity reading is likely to be within the range 1,008–1,015. Neither original nor final gravity figures are directly convertible to alcohol content by volume, due to the gradual changes which take place in real ale in particular as it matures. As a rough guide, though, because the figure given is based upon a comparison with water (the zero point), it can be seen that a wort with an original gravity of 1,048–1,052 is about five per cent more dense than water, so a guess at the figure of five per cent of alcohol by volume will be accurate enough for practical purposes.

Alcohol by volume is chosen because alcohol is lighter than water, making a 'by weight' comparison inverted and misleading.

To make a high accuracy check, an electronic calculator can be used to carry out the following simple arithmetic:

og 1,048, for example
final g 1,008, for example
divide the difference 0.40 by 0.0074

---

5.40 per cent alcohol by volume

---

The alcohol content of wine, cider and coolers is now indicated universally as a percentage of the drink's volume, most wines (including ginger wine) falling within the range ten to fifteen per cent, most fortified wines such as sherry and port within the range fifteen to twenty-five per cent, most ciders from four to ten per cent and most coolers from 2.5 to five per cent. Spirits are now rarely classified in degrees proof and generally by ABV.

Proof spirit was defined as that strength of alcohol which, if poured over a spoonful of gunpowder and ignited, would leave the powder just dry enough to remain explosive, i.e. independently combustible. Lower concentrations of alcohol would leave the powder wet and incapable of burning. This apparently complicated process was, in fact, very effective, but it is more simply understood by memorizing the detail that 'proof level' represents 57.1 per cent alcohol by volume. Percentage by volume will eventually replace proof spirit in Britain and Europe, and most producers seem to have converted, although some American spirits, such as bourbon (a whiskey), occasionally appear with proof spirit markings.

Just to complicate matters, the American proof system is calculated on a different basis, resulting in a higher figure for the same amount of alcohol than that quoted for degrees proof UK.

To convert alcohol by volume to degrees proof, multiply by 1.75 for degrees proof UK and by 2.0 for degrees proof USA.

Example:      alcohol by vol.      12 per cent
                      degrees proof UK      21
                      degrees proof USA    24

Conversely, to convert degrees proof UK and degrees proof USA to alcohol by volume, divide by 1.75 and 2.0 respectively. In Britain therefore, 100 per cent alcohol is 175 degrees proof.

There is a good deal more to producing healthy, tasty drinks than developing large amounts of alcohol in them – it takes little skill to produce a foul-tasting equivalent of rocket fuel, rather than wine, for example.

## The Pleasure and the Pain (Hangovers)

For a severe hangover, take the juice of two quarts of whisky.

Eddie Condon

Scientists are familiar with Newton's third Law of Motion, which says that, 'Every force has an opposing force.' This law appears, unfortunately for the drinker, to hold good in terms of alcoholic drinks – or, at least, in terms of the drinker's behaviour: the more you enjoy of your chosen beverage or beverages, the less you enjoy being alive the next day!

A hangover is mainly the result of consuming too much alcohol, although it may vary in severity according to such factors as sex, mood and body size of the drinker, the amount and type of food eaten prior to the drinking-session, and bodily metabolism, the latter dictating to some extent the final degree of dehydration. These factors are affected by additives in drinks, which may act as congeners boosting the effect of alcohol, which is a volatile hydrocarbon – that is, when heated, it is given off as vapour, the property which distillation of spirit drinks exploits.

Alcohol is treated by the human body as a slow-acting source of energy, which is why it is not possible to 'run off' the effects of over-indulgence in the same way as carbohydrates can be used to give energy to an athlete, for example. Before the alcohol in the bloodstream can be converted to energy, it must first be processed in the liver and kidneys. Physiologically, a hangover is caused by the inability of the body to cope with an overdose or backlog of alcohol and, taking the above variable factors into account as well, only when that versatile organ, the liver, has done its work will the headache, nausea and foul taste in the mouth disappear.

The liver becomes 'tired' after the first hour or so of attempting to break down and remove what is essentially a toxin (a poison), and it starts to slow down. Continuing to drink beyond this point results in a steady approach to inebriation, loss of faculties and eventually dehydration and brain-cell shrinkage, the main cause of the hangover headache. The brain loses water because of the diuretic effect of alcohol.

Doctors note the amount of free alcohol in the blood as a guide to drunkenness (the level rises as liver function declines) with a concentration of 1.25 mg per cent taken as the benchmark. This means 1.25 mg of alcohol in every hundredth part of a person's blood quantity. Two wines, two pints or two whiskies could make a person drunk (especially if that person is a small woman in a depressed state), producing in some cases a concentration of 4 mg alcohol per cent.

Because of the variation in volume of blood from person to person, legal (judicial) levels are taken as a sample of blood and not the total, unless the checker happens to be a vampire, presumably, which perhaps means the removal of all the person's blood. In Britain the legal limit for the driver of a car, based upon these levels, is 80 mg of alcohol in every 100 ml of blood. In Spain and Sweden, no alcohol must be found in a driver's bloodstream. How the authorities square this in relation to the minute amounts of alcohol created in the body by natural means is not clear, but amounts may be too small to register on electronic breathalysers or in subsequent analysis.

Although in theory a healthy liver should be able to detoxicate one alcohol unit per hour, in practice even such a liver will slow down. Theories – some of them useful – about alcohol include the swallowing of egg yolks to clear a hangover, but this is the cart bolting before the horse. An egg swallowed before drinking helps to coat the stomach with protein, slowing down absorption of the alcohol, but eggs are no special cure; almost any high protein foods will do. In the wake of the salmonella 'scare', eggs are probably not now a highly popular choice, however.

You could try Eddie Condon's 'cure' (see above) but the old hair-of-the-dog technique, which involves drinking a moderate amount of the drink which generated the hangover, usually on the morning after the binge, has never worked for me, and I know a few people who have been rendered virtually unconscious by the activity. THERE IS NO QUESTION BUT THAT IT IS DANGEROUS.

Perhaps it worked for Eddie Condon because of the disjointed segments of time which life meant for a jazz musician in the 1940s, consisting of all-night sessions and days spent travelling hundreds of miles on trains.

The only certain cures for a hangover are time and abstinence, although if you know you have drunk too much (not always easy to judge), the severity of the headache and nausea can be reduced by drinking about a quart of water 'before retiring', as the instruction used to go on the medicine bottles many years ago.

If you were drinking cider or beer earlier in the evening, this is no mean feat but can pay dividends, by preventing some of the dehydration which causes the pain. Whether you have drunk beer, wine or spirits to a potentially painful level will make very little difference to the sleepless night you are in for. Alcohol is a diuretic, meaning that it stimulates bladder and kidney function. 'All our drinks contain Vitamin P', explains a sign in a pub.

Drinking a lot of water may ease the pain the next day but will add to the diuretic effect, causing frequent nocturnal trips to the plumbing. Some of the general weakness felt the next morning is due to essential vitamins and nutrients being lost from the body, because of the flushing action of alcohol, but at least an 'overdose' of water the night before does seem to help.

Food scientists and nutritionists have tried to isolate and tabulate the essential chemistry of a hangover, but so far only the rather vague unit called a 'congener' or 'congener alcohol' has emerged to focus attention on a personal phenomenon which, in spite of thousands of years of self-induced suffering, is still only half-understood.

Some drinks, they have noted, seem to produce the worst hangovers. These include dark, sweet ales, red wine and dark spirits such as whisky and dark rum, all preceded in severity of effect by port. These drinks invariably contain significant quantities of isobutanol (butyl alcohol), which is responsible for much of a drink's flavour, along with esters. Scrumpy ('real ale' cider) is also credited with a high hangover potential, probably due to its sometimes high (compared with beer) methanol content, combined with its generally higher volume of ethyl alcohol. In general the stronger the taste of a drink, the more likely it is to produce a hangover.

Many additives to drinks also behave as congeners and may add to the high hangover potential of methanol and/or isobutanol.

Other theories point to unfermented components of drinks as causes of dehydration and severe hangover symptoms. One explanation suggests that the drinker's body continues to ferment this material while it is being broken down in the intestinal tract.

The fact that it is the darker or sweeter drinks which seem to produce the worst hangovers lends support to this theory. The semi-official list of drinks, declining in terms of their power to generate a hangover, is: port, brandy, whisky, dark rum, sherry, strong scrumpy cider, strong dark ale, barley wine, strong lager, premium-strength bitter ale, white spirits (vodka, gin, white rum), white wine, light bitter ale, light lager, alcohol-free drinks. Some drinkers would reverse the order on light drinks, with light rum and vodka producing the least discomfort.

## Surprise, Surprise!

Some people claim to experience 'surprise' hangovers. The usual explanation is 'I drank more than I wanted to', closely followed by 'I didn't realize the punch was alcoholic', but occasionally I hear that very little was consumed of anything, although a few bits of various drinks were tried, resulting in an 'unfair' punishment the next morning.

There's an old expression which probably covers the causes of this type of hangover: 'Never mix the hop and the grape.' It's not just the different types of drinks which I believe are responsible for the ultimate pain, but the presence of sulphur dioxide in each. First, sulphur dioxide begins to work upon proteins, destroying vitamin $B_1$. Add the dehydrating effect of alcohol itself, tot up the sulphur dioxide in the beer, the wine and perhaps the cider or a preservative such as benzoic acid in the soft drink the punch was made from, and you are in trouble.

Benzoic acid can have effects upon asthmatics which are similar to those of sulphur dioxide, so if it generates a headache as well, the chances are that you have taken a triple or quadruple dose of the two additives.

Further, you may have consumed a heavily carbonated drink, such as champagne or a sparkling white wine in the punch (or perhaps prior to the party), meaning that you have swallowed a good deal of carbon dioxide.

Now this gas, when taken into the stomach, can increase the secretion of gastric acids, promoting absorption of liquid by the mucous membrane. The result is a faster assimilation of alcohol. Doctors know that DTs (delirium tremens) can be limited in its effects, as can a severe hangover, by an intravenous injection of vitamin $B_1$, so if we take the inverse rule to be the case, you have had a quadruple dose of preservatives, you have absorbed alcohol much more quickly than you intended (due to the action of carbonated drinks) and you have mixed your 'breeds', while suffering a reduction in an essential vitamin. Your drinking-habits leave something to be desired!

Changes in substances called 'free radicals', which are formed within cells as a normal part of enzyme activity, may be the reason why some drinkers suffer more liver damage than others. A report in *Laboratory News* of February 1989, based on research carried out by Professor Timothy Peters of the King's College School of Medicine and Dentistry, notes vitamin E deficiency in alcohol-abusers. However, it is not yet known whether the deficiency affects free radical activity, causing greater damage, or if the deficiency is itself the result of high alcohol consumption.

All such effects, the teetotaller might argue, are avoidable, but it is clear that persistent over-indulgence can be cured, rather as though it were an infectious disease, if an item published in *Modern Domestic Medicine* in 1832 is to be believed:

Baron Cramer and a German physician of the name of Röth, have highly praised the following medicine as a valuable remedy for tippling and drunkenness. Dr Röth says that he has succeeded with this medicine in completely curing many poor creatures, both men and women, who were actually killing themselves by this practice. I hope that many in this country addicted to this baneful habit will try it and find it effectual. Take of tincture of columba one teaspoonful;

tincture of cascarilla one teaspoonful; compound tincture of gentian one teaspoonful; infusion of quassia a wineglassful; elixir of vitriol twenty drops. Mix and take twice a day and have a jug of cold water dashed over the head every morning on coming out of bed, and the feet bathed in warm water every night. Continue this for six or eight weeks.

The cold water torture sounds a bit drastic, but at least this recipe for the elimination of the desire to drink alcohol did not involve being soundly thrashed with birch twigs, as so many 'cures' of the time seemed to. I think that, on balance, I shall stick to an occasional swig of the demon drink – it sounds less punishing.

## The 'Designer Enzyme'

In addition to the singular relationship with alcohol which human gullet absorption represents, we have a specific bodily aid in the processing of the substance. Alcohol dehydrogenase, a liver enzyme, has the sole function of breaking down alcohol and appears to have evolved partly due to our ritual and social use of alcohol over many centuries but also because tiny amounts are produced by the body itself. Men possess larger amounts of the enzyme (also present in the stomach) than women, perhaps explaining their higher tolerance of alcohol.

The foregoing recipe to combat boozing is probably not now endorsed by the Royal College of Physicians, who recommend a more carefully weighed approach to alcohol intake levels.

Their advice, which is based upon an assumed three alcohol-free days per week, suggests the following 'safe level' intakes:

Men: maximum of 21 alcohol units per week.

Women and young adults: maximum of 14 alcohol units per week.

One alcohol unit, amounting to about eight to ten grams of pure alcohol, is found in half a pint of ale, lager or cider, a single whisky, a glass of sherry, a glass of wine etc.

The different maximum levels are stipulated because women and young adults have less blood (and therefore less water) in their bodies than men, added to the fact that their bodily systems are more susceptible to toxins, due in turn to the fact that their organs (kidneys, liver, brain) are likely to be smaller than those of an adult male. Because men have more water and less fat in their bodies, alcohol is diluted to some extent, compared with women.

These levels are guidelines only and should not be taken as an endorsement of regular moderate drinking – only the individual can decide the extent to which bodily and mental performance is affected by alcohol. Alcoholic cirrhosis (replacement of liver cells by fatty tissue) is irreversible and often fatal. It occurs due to consuming more alcohol than the liver can process, this level depending upon variable factors such as body size, metabolic rate and the general physical condition of the drinker.

Although the occasional binge (as long as it *is* occasional) will have no lasting effects, this type of heavy irregular drinking is said to kill more brain cells than regular drinking, and is thought to increase the risk of strokes.

The so-called diat pils lagers present a rather confusing problem where the estimation of physical effects is concerned. They are intended for diabetics and not for weight-reduction diets, as their name may seem to imply. While alcohol is marginally more acceptable to a diabetic than raw sugars (carbohydrates), it is in fact considerably the more fattening of the two substances if you take calories into account.

The Food Labelling Regulations 1984 assume the following energy-conversion factors:

1 gram of fat shall be deemed to contribute 37 kilojoules (9 kilocalories).

1 gram of alcohol shall be deemed to contribute 29 kilojoules (7 kilocalories).

1 gram of protein shall be deemed to contribute 17 kilojoules (4 kilocalories).

1 gram of carbohydrate (expressed as monosaccharides – simple sugars) shall be deemed to contribute 16 kilojoules (3.7 kilocalories).*

In spite of frequent warnings about the dire consequences of abuse, however, it seems that giving up alcoholic drinks (or never starting to drink them) offers no particular health benefits. A Royal College of Physicians report carries the conclusion that, 'Abstainers do not necessarily enjoy better health than moderate drinkers.'

---

* One kilocalorie = the amount of heat required to raise 1 kg of water by 1°C.

There are some areas where abstinence is to be encouraged. Pregnant women should not drink alcohol at all. The risk is to the unborn child, which may suffer the effects of foetal alcohol syndrome. Affected babies are small, often deformed and brain-damaged.

If you are taking any kind of medication for any kind of complaint, you should not drink. In combination with alcohol, some drugs and medicines, whether in pill, fluid or injected forms, can kill. Sleeping-pills are especially dangerous in this context because, like alcohol, they are hypnotics – that is, they depress central nervous system activity. Antibiotics may be rendered inactive if you drink while taking them, and dizziness and sleepiness are twin symptoms associated with a mixture of alcohol and penicillin, for example. Don't mix them – ever!

The early twentieth-century movement for abstinence and persistent modern warnings about the 'dangers' of drinking alcohol, each of the latter seeming to contradict the immediate previous findings, may have had a prototype in a cautionary tale from ancient Egypt included in material released by Lord Carnavon's family. Carnavon was the archaeologist who discovered and excavated Tutankamun's tomb, and among the hieroglyphic fragments he brought back was an outline on papyrus called *The Precepts of Ani*, a book of etiquette from about 1500 BC. This contains the following warning about the social consequences of over-indulgence: 'Make not thyself helpless in drinking in the beer-shop. For will not the words of thy report slip out from thy mouth without thou knowing that thou hast uttered them? Falling down, thy limbs will be broken and no one will help thee up. As for thy companions in the swilling of beer, they will say "Outside with this drunkard." '

## Boozers and Behaviour

There can hardly be anyone in Britain or Europe today who has not heard that nonsensical (in grammatical terms) phrase 'football violence'. It is difficult to see how a leather ball can be violent; the violence attaches, of course, to the football fans themselves and not to the game or the players.

There is no hard-and-fast evidence I can point to in order to support this assertion, but my experience has shown that the generally loutish behaviour which gives rise to this concern is due to one of the less sociable aspects of alcohol – its tendency to induce aggressive behaviour. Physiologically this is due to effects where alcohol works to diminish the 'censor' activity of the brain – that set of social conventions and moral constraints which (in general) keep people civilized and passive.

It seems to be midday (or all-day) drinking which induces the strongest aggressive responses. This may be due in part to the higher metabolic rate at which the drinker's body works during the midday period, and perhaps also because of the general sense of malaise felt as the subject suffers the depressant effects of alcohol on the nervous system, giving rise in turn to feelings of social dissonance. Because of these effects, all-day drinking can induce in some people a highly aggressive or agitated state, but whether the all-day opening of British licensed premises, which became legal on 22 August 1988, will have a major impact upon general levels of drunkenness and drink-related behaviour may not be clear for several years.

According to a report in the *Daily Telegraph* of 18 September 1989, many licensees had changed their minds about staying open for twelve hours a day. The newspaper quoted the Brewers' Society as saying that fifty per cent of licensees who had tried longer hours initially had reverted to restricted hours one year later, though some in city centres and at tourist spots would stick to 'liberal' hours because of vastly increased business and cash flow.

The conclusion seems to be, however, that alcohol intake has risen in the city centres. Fortunately, drinking seems to make some people doze off rather than making them aggressive.

The answer to drink-related problems lies not in a ban on alcohol, but in the education of drinkers in the effects of the substance and ways of limiting them.

## Practical Methods of Alcohol Limiting

There are a few practical methods which can help to cut or control the committed drinker's intake:

* Don't keep large quantities of drink at home. Easily accessible drinks, especially those you prefer, can be an irresistible temptation, especially if you happen to work at home. As long as drinking is a social activity and not a solitary one, there are always some constraints at work upon your behaviour.

* Take a week off booze every month, and try always to confine your drinking to no more than four days in any week. This way you can keep within the recommended health limits and enjoy the drink as well. That week off may well convince you to try abstinence for a longer period, and these periods 'off the booze' will give your body time to recover from 'heavy sessions' related to a professional working lifestyle in particular. Doctors and journalists top the league of those most at risk from this professional hazard, and it may need a good deal of will-power to say 'no' when invited to a lunch or dinner which you know will feed and wine you magnificently.

* Gradually reduce the amount you drink in company with others. Try a single rather than a double, and follow it with an astringent fruit juice such as orange or grapefruit – this inhibits the appetite for more fluid.

* Pace your drinking. Take it slowly and never gulp or 'knock back' drinks in one. This practice is bad for your head, your love life, your liver and your pocket!

* Don't 'chase' spirits with long drinks or make use of hair-of-the-dog or proprietary brand hangover 'cures' – these habits are dangerous.

* Keep a daily or a weekly log of the number of alcohol units you drink – the figures may surprise you!

* Never drink on an empty stomach. Any food taken before a drinking-session will help to slow absorption and limit the possible damage to the mucous membrane of the stomach, but high protein or fatty foods will provide the greatest protection.

* Don't drink neat spirits. They do not make you drunk quicker and cause greater structural damage to the gullet and stomach, as well as posing a higher risk of cancer-generation.

* Try to make an accurate appraisal of your drinking-habits. If you drink at lunchtime as well as in the evening, it would be wise to cut the midday habit, when your body runs at a high metabolic rate, causing faster assimilation and greater damage.

## Old Soak's Charter or Temperance Text?

As a drinker myself, I admit to a liking for alcohol, but I think I know my limits. However, the fact remains that nobody can tell you exactly how much you can drink safely if you are to continue to enjoy the habit, nor can they estimate accurately the precise effects of alcohol and/or additives upon your body or your likely lifespan as a drinker.

The extent of effects between individuals may vary enormously, as do the opinions of doctors, scientists and alcohol-problem advisers. Only *you* can decide which aspects are hurting you, although you cannot tell what is happening to your liver – hence the guidelines on intake based on 'units'. Your decision will be more effective if it includes balanced advice from many sources.

Because of variable human factors, most doctors are forced into making generalizations about the effects of alcohol, peppered with emotive bursts of conviction that, 'Booze is a killer' or alternatively that, 'A little of what you fancy does you good.'

These swings in opinion occur because human beings stubbornly refuse to behave in a predictable or uniform chemical/medical sense, one person's body being able to withstand decades of abuse, while another succumbs to only a small amount of alcohol or other addictive material.

In her book *The Demon Drink*, Jancis Robinson points to what she suggests are insignificant figures for deaths from alcoholic cirrhosis of the liver, compared with those from tobacco or heroin:

| | |
|---|---|
| Tobacco: | 571 people in every 100,000 |
| Heroin: | 783 per 100,000 |
| Alcohol: | 25 per 100,000 |

Such figures, presented in such a way, can be dangerously seductive for the uncommitted drinker, although I am sure this was not the author's intention.

Extrapolating these figures results in a total of 10,000 deaths among the 40 million people in Britain who drink alcohol. This may seem insignificant when compared with the death rate from coronary heart disease (around 150,000 people annually), which is also exacerbated by moderate drinking, but if you happen to be one of those 10,000 people experiencing a long, lingering death in a hospital ward, your view of booze is likely to shift a little!

Official figures for heroin deaths are hard to come by, unlike a detail which points to the drinks industry's powerful political connections. In 1989 more than fifty British MPs had financial interests in the drinks industry (which they declared in the Commons Register).

The interested observer can make a note in the margin about another revealing detail. In 1986 the HEC (Health Education Council) published its *Guide to Healthy Eating*, which, among other recommendations, advised that 'Sugar gives you "empty calories" – that is, calories with no other nutrients: no vitamins, no minerals, no fibre, no protein ... aim to cut down the amount of sugar you eat by a half.'

The HEC's director, Dr David Player, publicly expressed the view that 'the alcohol industry is even more powerful in its effect on government decisions than the tobacco industry.' Such overt interest in the health of the consumer brought predictable retribution: in November 1986 the Cabinet Minister responsible, Norman Fowler, abolished the HEC, and in March 1987 he also abolished the JACNE (Joint Advisory Committee on Nutrition Education), which had helped with the HEC's guide. The replacement for these two bodies is the Health Education Authority, which comes under indirect government control!

In spite of the commonsense inherent in some doctors' orders, they are not necessarily immutable commandments inscribed on tablets of stone, which the bewildered drinker ignores at his or her peril. One indication of this need for caution came in 1988, when the BMA (British Medical Association) decided to withdraw its campaign against alcohol advertising. It seems that members had realized that they might, should they accept such a policy, have to close down the BMA Wine Club, which sells wines to doctors at discount rates and organizes trips to the European vineyards.

# CASK, KEG AND CASE STUDIES

# 3  Beer

The brewer's art is like a butler's boxe at Christmasse – it is sure to
winne, whosoever loses.

Puritan essay, 1621

## The Beer Necessities

Anyone who works at the treatment of people suffering with the
effects of alcoholism will know of the relatively low food value
of most alcoholic drinks.

General debility is the most common physical symptom in
sufferers, because they tend to eat very little, resulting in
protein- and vitamin-deficiencies.

Probably the most nutritious of all alcoholic drinks is beer, but
only in its real ale form. Keg beers, which are filtered and
pasteurized, do not have as much food value. Additive-free
wine and home-brewed versions of all forms of beer and wine
are also better in a nutritional sense than mass-produced forms.

Real ale, however, seems to be the best 'food drink' because,
in addition to its high water-content, which includes a few
beneficial minerals, such a beer provides carbohydrate for
energy (about 180 calories per pint of average bitter or lager) as
well as traces of acids, vitamins and oils, but its most nutritious
component is the yeast which remains in suspension in the
fluid.

Yeast contains several vitamins, notably those of the B
complex, which includes folic acid, nicotinic acid (niacin), biotin
and pyridoxine (vitamin $B_6$) and is a rich source of vitamin $B_1$
(thiamin). Without sufficient B complex vitamins, pellagra, the
famous malnutrition disease of the southern USA at the turn of
the nineteenth–twentieth century can occur. Home-brewed
beers, ciders, wines and perries may all contain these vitamins
in yeast if they are not in any way processed after fermentation.

Vitamin $B_6$ is essential for healthy skin, nerves and blood. Lack of it can cause severe anaemia and, in infants, convulsions, although I hesitate to recommend that beer should replace milk in babies' feeding-bottles. An accurate label description for keg ale or lager might read: 'Contains hop extracts, degraded proteins and sugars, E150(c) ammonia caramel, E405 propylene glycol alginate, E220 sulphur dioxide, no vitamins.'

In view of the FAC's comments on the white-cell destroying capability (in rats) of E150(c) ammonia caramel, but only in the absence of sufficient vitamin $B_6$, it may be that real ales and home-brew of all forms contain their own built-in antidote to this effect. It is by no means certain, however, that effects seen in rats will be duplicated in human beings.

Keg beers, a group which includes processed versions of ale, stout and lager as well as most ciders, possess little food value, for any yeast (containing vitamins) content is destroyed by pasteurization. But the big brewers are not concerned with food value. Their 'national brands' are works of art aided by science. These delicious-looking golden, brown and black alcoholic fluids are created by brewing cosmetics experts, who design them primarily for eye-appeal. You might say they exercise a form of genius in this activity, but the skilled use of a brown stain is hardly an example of pure genius!

Each of the major brewers (and many of the major winemakers) has an army of chemists and a bewildering array of substances at his command in the battle to make his national brands more beautiful to look at than the products of the principal opposition. The proof of these beauties is in the drinking, however. When you get the painted blonde home, she often disappoints at the moment of taste – off comes the wig, and bang goes the wooden leg as the drinker swallows a mouthful of gas and a glassful of nothingness. But that's not all! Independent analyses carried out in 1986 discovered aluminium and formaldehyde in samples of British beer. Aluminium is often a constituent of domestic water supplies because of the use of alum (aluminium sulphate) as a fining medium, although in this form it is not readily metabolized by the human body, so it poses few if any risks, but formaldehyde is not so innocuous. The presence of this substance, which is a possible carcinogen, is *almost certainly due to the use of additive 900 dimethylpolysiloxane, which functions as a foam-control agent during fermentation.* Used as a food additive, this substance may legally contain up to 100 mg of formaldehyde per kilo.

This dubious additive is used solely to enhance the brewer's economy. Because most lager fermentations (and many ale fermentations) are now carried out in closed containers called 'conical fermenters', these brewers employ additive 900 in order to maximize the available space in the fermenter, producing a higher yield.

According to *Brewing Review* for February 1987, additive 900 is 'removed from beer prior to packaging, by absorption on yeast or by filters'. This claim conflicts with the opinion of several independent brewers, who consider the substance to be 'extremely dangerous' and assert that they would not use it under any conditions.

To be fair, the greater part of the big brewer's additives armoury is employed before brewing in order to boost the performance of the natural raw materials. Gibberellic acid and starch-breaking enzymes are typical of this preparatory treatment, and most such materials help to maintain consistent flavour and appearance. They are thus, however, used almost exclusively as an aid to sales, based upon public perceptions concerning appearance.

At the other extreme, the small and independent breweries depend for their continued success upon demand fed by value judgements which revolve around taste and choice, so they use fewer additives, or none at all, being prepared to allow the character and flavour of their beers to change a little.

The argument for commercial success based upon giving the consumers what they want (or have been conditioned to accept) collapses when the situation in Western Germany is considered. While seemingly innocuous materials such as flaked maize and ground rice are used by some British and American brewers to improve head-retention in their beers, these cereal adjuncts are seldom if ever used by German brewers producing beer for the home market, mainly because of a German Federal Standard for beer ingredients and methods which has held sway for 470 years but is now being gradually eroded.

Until the spring of 1988, when an EEC 'directive' made it clear that its provisions were no longer legally binding upon member states, the Reinheitsgebot (beer purity law) remained in absolute control of brewers' activities where the home-drunk product was concerned, but not in terms of German beers brewed for export. Most lagers brewed for export, for example, cannot be considered 'pure' and have been described as 'cocktails of additives', although there is a growing number of notable exceptions from small breweries.

Duke Wilhelm IV of Bavaria drew up the purity law in 1516 with the aim of combating the growing tendency of brewers to adulterate their beers with synthetic bittering or body-enhancing materials, sometimes with fatal results for drinkers. The code of practice became a Federal Standard in the 1950s. It stipulates that nothing other than malt, water, hops and yeast may be used in the brewing of beer.

The EEC 'directive' of March 1988 may have been the result of foreign pressure to regularize trade in the lead-up to the wider market thrust of 1992. Certainly, the purity law has been coming under increasing attack from British and American drinks giants who interpret its provisions as being aimed at the unfair protection of the German brewing industry, in the face of foreign competition. This new pressure may also be due to the realization that British, American and Australian brewers could never hope to compete in terms of purity – they have too much to lose.

Evidence that German brewers are responding to this pressure can be seen in the relaxation of their previously tight control over imports of beer, permitting stout in particular to be imported. Draught Guinness Export is now available in several bars in the Braunschweig (Brunswick) area. This export stout is not available in the UK and is said to have been brewed in Dublin to the Reinheitsgebot standard.

However, it is the keg versions of ale, stout and lager which have the major slice of beer sales in Britain, and the suggestion that a purity law should be introduced would probably generate a howl of protest from the big brewers, who are quite happy, thank you, to carry on adding the heading-agents and preservatives to their organically dead beers, humming happily all the way to the bank.

If any of the big brewers in Britain should comment that, to coin an old adage, 'Competition is more effective than legislation', they should bear in mind that by the end of 1989 there were 860 breweries operating in Bavaria alone, showing that pure beer can be profitable.

Most of Germany's 1,200 breweries, and especially the home-brew inns and bars of the south-east, brew 'real ale lager'

which is unfiltered, unpasteurized and lacking in preservatives*
other than hops. Many of these beers are served 'on gravity'
from large wooden hogsheads. In contrast, there were 208 listed
breweries in operation in Britain in 1989, seven having closed in
the previous year, and of this total, a hundred were (and are)
owned by the big eight brewing combines or are subsidiaries of
these brewing giants. The famous Ruddles of Oakham, Rutland,
is now owned by Watney, for example.

It is hardly possible to go up to any pub bar in Britain without
meeting one or two examples of English, Scottish and American
derivatives of the classic German lagers. The majority of these
boast Teutonic-sounding names, but they are local (to Britain)
concoctions which have only a fleeting resemblance to the
original or are brewed 'under licence'. None of these lagers can
be considered additive-free (with two exceptions, see Survey 1).

On the other hand, the Reinheitsgebot applies only to beers
for consumption in Germany, and many of those which are
exported would fall within the category which covers most
English, Scottish, French and 'Australian' lagers – *chemibier*, as
the German brewers call it. Furthermore, following a decision by
the European Court, German beer merchants may now import
additive-enriched (if that is an appropriate term) beer from
anywhere in the world.

Confusingly, some members of EEC food committees in
Brussels want to extend the purity law to all other member
states (which clearly includes Britain), although both France and
Italy maintain a partial purity law already. In these two
countries, any type of beer must be brewed from a minimum of
seventy and seventy-five per cent malt (as a percentage of the
grist) respectively, while in the Benelux countries a minimum of
sixty per cent malt is stipulated.

In Britain there are no minimum levels stipulated for any of
the main ingredients used in brewing. The only area covered by
anything remotely resembling the Reinheitsgebot is the Isle of
Man, where the Manx Pure Beer Act permits the use of sugar, in
addition to water, malt, hops and yeast.

With an annual consumption of beer per head in Germany of
360 pints, EEC committee members who wish to maintain and in

---

* Hops and malt may contain insecticide residues, making the
concept of 'green' beer nonsensical.

some cases strengthen the purity law will no doubt have in mind the possibility of a slow poisoning of the beer-drinking population, should it disappear.

German brewers were first called upon to account for their adherence to Duke Wilhelm's purity law at the European Court a few years ago, when the EEC commissioners wanted to know why the brewers would not reduce their standards to conform with those of brewers in, for example, Great Britain. This contradictory behaviour may be a characteristic of bureaucracies, but it gave rise to an illuminating exchange at the court. Germany's representative at the hearing, Martin Seidl, said that at least six synthetic substances (clearly forbidden by the purity law) had been found in beers brewed in Germany for export to Britain, but that no fewer than twenty-eight such dubious substances had been found in many British and Irish beers brewed for export to Germany.

Herr Seidl asked the court: 'Who knows what these substances, accumulating in the human body, may do?'

His question is perhaps a little sensationalist in that there is as yet no evidence to show that the principal additives, when used at the recommended levels, remain in the drinker for very long, although they certainly remain in the drinks.

A similar misconception, a widely held one at that, is that beer in particular is no longer a natural product and is 'just a load of chemicals'. The misconception lies in the fact that the basic raw materials of brewing and winemaking have not changed from those used by the Babylonians, although malt, water, hops, yeast and grapes, which are themselves composed of 'chemicals', as are the drinkers' bodies, are now augmented by many unnecessary substances.

This apparent pollution of the process and proceeds of fermentation is complicated by the effects of industrial and agricultural pollution, where sulphurous compounds are emitted by factory chimneys, the consequent 'acid rain'-type materials later finding their way into the food chain via water supplies and, in brewing, from well water.

One especially significant factor is the use by cereal farmers of so-called 'short straw' height-stunting additives to the barley growing in the fields. This material, by restricting the height of the barley stalks, produces fatter grains, which yield more maltose eventually, but some maltsters report worrying increases in the nitrate content of malting barley. This higher level requires cautious kilning of barley in order to limit the generation of nitrosamines.

Bearing these factors in mind, a drinker may ask how a definition of pure beer, wine or cider can be approached, but these factors already exist for the greater part of the 'food chain', so we seem to be stuck with them, but we can at least aim for drinks which are fermented and processed using the minimum of additives. In this case a drinker should be able to decide upon a definition of pure wine, beer or cider, based upon the same assumption made in concluding that a water supply is pure: that it is unlikely to cause disease. Again, 'pure genius' is not the term that springs to mind where the manufacture of drinks is concerned!

With an annual consumption per head of 250 pints of beer and 10.8 litres (approximately twenty pints) of wine in Britain, value judgements concerning purity are important.

In the USA, which is considered by many British real-ale drinkers to be devoid of the real thing, let alone the pure thing (the keg process for beer rules supreme), there have been heartening signs of a revival in good brewing. One sign of progress is the microbrewery, where real ale and real lager are brewed. Though most of the microbreweries' beers are forced up to the pump by carbon dioxide top pressure, some are bottled and naturally conditioned. Examples of the range available include Samuel Adams Lager and Dock Street Amber, brewed from amber malt, which is now rare in Britain and Europe. The most famous new brew is probably Eau Claire Lager, brewed in Wisconsin solely from malt, water, hops and yeast, *à la* Reinheitsgebot.

The microbrewery family had grown from only twelve in 1983 to 110 in 1988, and analysts have predicted that there would be 250 such small breweries in the USA by the end of 1989.

## Learnin' the Brews

'In the beginning was the wort.'

Anon.

Brewing is a very old craft. The Roman historian Pliny recorded in his *Natural History* how the natives of Gaul and Spain brewed barley-based alcoholic drinks, which he termed *celia* or *ceria* and sometimes *cerevisia* or *cervisia*, all these forms being embodied in the Latin name for top-fermenting ale yeasts – saccharomyces cerevisiae.

Although mead, fermented from honey and water, is the world's oldest alcoholic drink (possibly 10,000 years old), something resembling ale was brewed nearly 7,000 years ago by the Mesopotamians and certainly by the Egyptians who, according to Pliny, drank a beverage he called *zythum*, brewed from an infusion of barley malt. 'The people of Spain in particular brew this liquor so well that it will keep good a long time,' he wrote. 'So exquisite is the cunning of mankind in gratifying his vicious appetites that he has thus invented a method to make water itself produce intoxification.'

It was not quite as Pliny thought. While water was (and still is) the principal constituent of most alcoholic drinks, there was always much more to intoxification than the use of the cheapest drink material on earth. Whether he was worried about the materials used to produce the drinks of his time is not recorded, although the Romans are known to have used sulphur dioxide, extracted by the treatment of sulphur, to preserve their wine.

Brewing is thought to have begun more by accident than design. Corn (maize-type) cereals having been a staple food for these early civilizations (but with little risk of excess nitrate contamination), there was plenty of material available for an accidental discovery to be made, and the first ale copied from a natural effect. Barley, which was cultivated by the Egyptians, had reached Europe by 3000 BC, and a mix of cereal 'porridge' and water, left in a warm spot, might develop a dizzying after-effect when drunk, airborne yeasts having fermented sugars in this crude ale mash.

Another possibility is that primitive peoples discovered that, by chewing fruit and then spitting out the salivated material, it would soon ferment. This would result from the enzyme amylase, which is present in human saliva, converting the fruit starches into fermentable sugars. Some tribes of Amazonian Indians continue to ferment a strong drink in this way, using the fruit of the guava tree as the base material.

An Egyptian *bas relief* carving in the Leiden Museum, in the Netherlands, dated at about 2300 BC shows brewing in progress. Barley was first soaked in wet soil until the grains swelled. They were then washed and ground to a paste, the resulting dough being baked, producing malt loaf. Pieces of the loaf were then mixed with water. The malty infusion which resulted from this complicated (and possibly mystical) process was then strained into stone jars where fermentation would begin spontaneously after a few days. Later this unhopped, and probably rather sour, ale was matured in large earthenware jugs sealed with clay.

In spite of fears that modern commercially brewed beers are 'synthetic' or 'chemical' concoctions, at the initial stages the same materials, plant and methods continue in use today. The monastery brewers of Norman times rationalized brewing techniques, and the Victorians mechanized them in their tower breweries, where each function was aided by gravity and pulleys. Modern ergonomically designed plant extends these methods to the point now known as 'the keg process'.

The result of this process is the conversion to 'long-life beer' of natural ale, stout and lager. Keg beers are organically dead and incapable of further maturation, which natural process improves flavour and strength in real ales.

To brew beer, all one has to do is keep barley grains (or wheat grains) warm in moist conditions until they begin to grow. The resulting malt grain is crushed in a mill to produce the grist (hence 'grist to the mill'), which is then steeped in water ('mashed') at a temperature around 65°C (150°F), converting the starch and protein content of each grain into an infusion of malt. The liquid mixture (the 'wort' – pronounced 'wert') is then boiled with hops, and sometimes sugar, and later cooled through a series of pipes called a 'paraflow'. Yeast is then added ('pitched'), starting a natural fermentation. At the end of the ferment, which may take up to a week, the beer is racked (syphoned) from the sediment and matured in storage tanks.

All the large breweries in Britain, Europe, Australasia and North America extend this basic process by pasteurizing, chill filtering, carbonating and cooling most of their output, these life-extending methods being augmented by the use of preservatives and enzymes.

Many bottled or canned beers contain the latter substances, many of which are derived from the action of cultured bacteria on sugar, or extracted from vegetable sources. Ficin is obtained from the inedible latex (rubber-like resin) of a tree, as is papain, which is extracted from the fruit of the pawpaw. These enzymes are used as an aid to chill-filtering, especially of lager, or are added to bottled or canned beer to counter haze formation during storage.

Beer-drinkers visiting Germany can check the phenomenon

for themselves by bringing back a few cans of a good German beer brewed to the purity standard, such as Andreas Pils, which is a product of the independent brewery of C.H. Andreas of Hagen, Westphalia. This strong lager beer (1,050 or 6 per cent ABV) – will develop a faint haze if stored for about three months, although no noticeable change will occur in flavour.

Some people who 'drink with their eyes' might jettison this misty-looking beer, but the chemical changes producing the haze are natural, unlike the inhibiting action of enzymes in star-bright canned beer, which are more suited to car tyre production!

Similarly, many German brewers, sticking rigidly to the purity law, do not carbonate their beers by artificial means, preferring to use the traditional method called *kräusen*. This involves adding a portion of vigorously fermenting wort (full of yeast) to green beer, producing condition (fizz) within a few hours or days, depending upon the yeast growth.

## Modern Developments

### HIGH GRAVITY BREWING

Some breweries produce beers, mainly for bottling, by means of a technique called 'high gravity brewing'. This technique, which is not in widespread use, involves fermentation of a wort at a very high original gravity, typically between og 1,300 and og 1,600, using high alcohol-tolerant yeasts. The resulting beer, which has an ABV content of fifteen to eighteen per cent, is then watered in the cask to the required strength for drinking.

Beers brewed in this way are said by tasters to be insipid and characterless and their main advantage is to the brewer, who makes savings in storage space and carriage costs, due to the product's being more compact and lighter in weight than 'normal' beers.

### BEER CONCENTRATES

A new development in high gravity brewing carries the process one stage farther, by taking the beer to the point of dispense before it is watered. The technique, as with other high gravity brewed beers, is confined to keg ('top pressure') brews, due to the difficulty of maintaining a head in beers transferred to secondary containers. Further new techniques may involve frozen, concentrated beers, which will be thawed out by the barman or licensee before they are dispensed.

The high gravity and beer concentrate techniques simplify excise duty measurement at the original gravity stage, since only one check is necessary, rather than the checking of the several brews that it replaces.

The following flow charts show each stage of the modern brewing process in use throughout the world. The diagrams include low and no-alcohol beer techniques. These techniques are also used to process low-alcohol ciders and wines – see pp.76-81.

## Basic beer types

### REAL ALE

Since the mid-1970s the term 'real ale' has come into general use, meaning beer which is brewed with a yeast which ferments at the top of the wort, the latter being the liquid mixture of malt, liquor (water) and other cereals or sugars. The wort is known as 'the sweet wort' before it is boiled with hops and 'the hopped wort' afterwards. Real-ale brewing proceeds through several natural stages and the beer is allowed to mature in a cask without further processing. It is often known as 'cask-conditioned ale' for this reason. While it matures, fresh unboiled hops may be added to the cask, producing a bittering effect in the beer which is subtly different from that achieved at the boil stage. This is called 'dry-hopping'. Real ale is served mainly via a handpump (a 'beer-engine') into the glass, or it may be dispensed on gravity – directly from the cask tap. It has a relatively short life in its natural state.

### KEG ALE

Brewed initially in the same way and from the same ingredients (malt, water, hops and yeast), keg ale is afterwards filtered, pasteurized (heated to destroy all living organisms including yeast), then carbonated under pressure in a keg. It is then cooled artificially and dispensed to the pump tap at the bar by carbon dioxide under pressure – so-called 'top pressure'. Both keg ale and keg lager have a less 'beery' flavour than real ale but both have a long life. Keg ale is described by brewers as 'brewery-conditioned ale'.

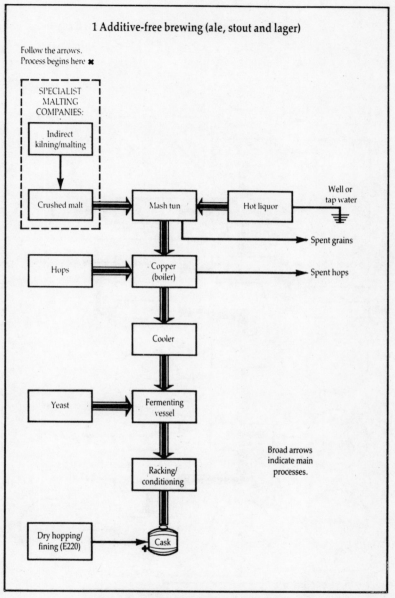

# 1 Additive-free brewing (ale, stout and lager)

Follow the arrows.
Process begins here ✖

SPECIALIST MALTING COMPANIES:

Indirect kilning/malting → Crushed malt → Mash tun ← Hot liquor ← Well or tap water

Mash tun → Spent grains

Hops → Copper (boiler) → Spent hops

Copper (boiler) → Cooler

Yeast → Fermenting vessel

Fermenting vessel → Racking/conditioning

Dry hopping/fining (E220) → Cask

Broad arrows indicate main processes.

1 Many of the small "boutique" breweries or "microbreweries" in Australia, Britain, Canada, Germany and the USA, employ the additive-free brewing method shown here. This technique extends the natural brewing process, and the only additional material to those stipulated in the German purity law is isinglass finings, which may contain trace quantities of E220 sulphur dioxide, as do some hops.

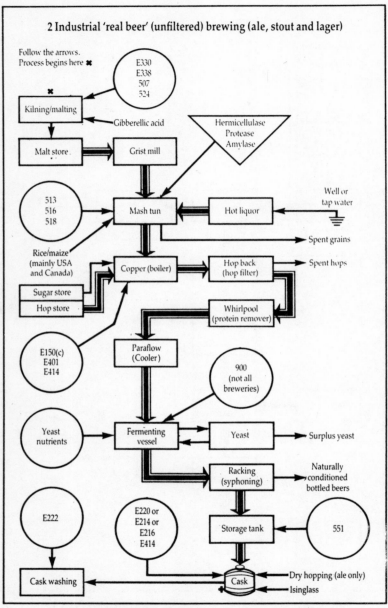

## 2 Industrial 'real beer' (unfiltered) brewing (ale, stout and lager)

Follow the arrows.
Process begins here ✖

E330
E338
507
524

Kilning/malting

Gibberellic acid

Hermicellulase
Protease
Amylase

Malt store → Grist mill

513
516
518

Mash tun ← Hot liquor ← Well or tap water

Spent grains

Rice/maize
(mainly USA
and Canada)

Copper (boiler) → Hop back (hop filter) → Spent hops

Sugar store

Hop store

Whirlpool (protein remover)

E150(c)
E401
E414

Paraflow (Cooler)

900
(not all breweries)

Yeast nutrients → Fermenting vessel ← Yeast → Surplus yeast

Racking (syphoning) → Naturally conditioned bottled beers

E222

E220 or
E214 or
E216
E414

Storage tank ← 551

Cask washing ← Cask ← Dry hopping (ale only)
← Isinglass

**2** The industrial process for unfiltered beers, shown here, is employed by the principal breweries in Australia, Britain, France, Germany and the USA. Most employ the full, additive-aided process. Additives are shown in circles at point of addition, enzymes in triangles. The term "sugar" refers to sucrose, glucose or brewers' (invert) sugar.

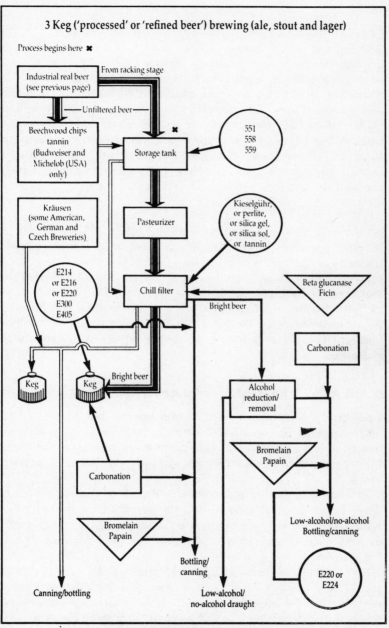

# 3 Keg ('processed' or 'refined beer') brewing (ale, stout and lager)

Process begins here ✖

**Industrial real beer** (see previous page)

From racking stage

— Unfiltered beer —

**Beechwood chips tannin** (Budweiser and Michelob (USA) only)

**Storage tank** ✖

551 558 559

**Kräusen** (some American, German and Czech Breweries)

**Pasteurizer**

Kieselgühr, or perlite, or silica gel, or silica sol, or tannin

E214 or E216 or E220 E300 E405

**Chill filter**

Beta glucanase Ficin

Bright beer

**Carbonation**

Keg

Keg

Bright beer

**Alcohol reduction/ removal**

**Bromelain Papain**

**Carbonation**

**Bromelain Papain**

Low-alcohol/no-alcohol Bottling/canning

E220 or E224

Canning/bottling

Bottling/ canning

Low-alcohol/ no-alcohol draught

**3** The so-called "keg" process follows up real beer methods by pasteurizing and/ or filtering the drink, the latter by extensive chill techniques and haze-breaking enzymes. The result is a bright beer with a very long life.

## LAGER

The lightest of the beers, in both colour and flavour, lager is brewed from a less strongly malted form of barley and fermented with a yeast which 'works' at the bottom of the container. Less bitter hops are employed in lager than in bitter and stout. These are generally the German variety called Hallertau or the Czech variety called Saaz, although some English lager brewers now use a new variety grown mainly in Kent and Hampshire, called Wye Challenger. Most draught lager in Britain is keg lager, unlike many German forms, which are 'real ale' lager.

## STOUT

A very dark top-fermented beer, stout is bitter and dry-tasting in its most popular form but relatively sweet in its form as porter, formerly a famous Victorian ale. Only Guinness Extra Stout brewed and sold in Ireland is 'real ale' stout – all the draught stout on sale in the rest of Britain is keg stout, with the exception of bottled Guinness Extra Stout, which is naturally conditioned (yeast remains in the bottle). Unlike most keg ales, Guinness or Draught Guinness is forced up to the bar by nitrogen under pressure.

## NABLABS – The Healthier Alternative?

Christmas 'wheelwatch' campaigns by the big brewers and endorsement of NABLABS (no-alcohol beers, low-alcohol beers), ciders and wines by government ministers, make these highly processed drinks the most strongly promoted of modern times.

It was Peter Bottomley, then the British Minister for Roads and Traffic, who, in 1988 coined the acronym for these drinks which, because they are below the 1.2 per cent ABV cut-off point in the 1984 regulations, must be labelled to show their ingredients.

Some labels on these drinks and others such as soft drinks and a few coolers reveal the extent to which additives are employed in the industry generally. Low- and no-alcohol beers, wines and ciders often contain as many strangely un-drink-like substances as full-strength versions. A typical ingredients label on a can of alcohol-free lager (which is likely to contain 0.06 per cent alcohol) contains information such as: 'Water, malt, sugar, wheatflour, hops, papain, carbon dioxide, aspartame, anti-oxidant E300, stabilizer E405.'

In this example, E405 propylene glycol alginate is described vaguely as a 'stabilizer'; its function is that of head-retaining agent, although a deviant etymologist might describe it as a 'foam-stabilizer'. Papain is an enzyme employed to degrade proteins in the lager, which might otherwise cause a haze to form during storage. E300 is ascorbic acid (vitamin C) which is included in order to counter the effects of the small amounts of air which enter the can or bottle during filling. This additive acts as an anti-oxidant, preventing flavour changes.

Wheatflour is added to give an illusion of 'body' in the drink, which has had most of its taste removed at the same time as most of the alcohol. Removal of ethyl alcohol, the main alcoholic constituent, is accomplished by several methods:

(a)     distillation, where the drink is heated, a process identical to the distilling of spirit drinks; the difference is that the distillate is discarded and the distilling medium retained;

(b)     reverse osmosis, which involves forcing the drink through a semi-permeable membrane (a fine filter). (This technique confers a health benefit, because it also filters out nitrates.);

(c)     shifting the pH factor of the wort or must (wine) in order to induce an ineffective fermentation;

(d)     the use of genetically altered yeasts, which ferment very slowly, producing little alcohol.

All such methods are applied equally to no- and low-alcohol wines and ciders, and after removing the alcohol, the brewer or winemaker can reclaim the revenue paid on it at the brewing stage, as though it were a 'spoiled brew', i.e. one which had become infected in the brewing or winemaking vessel. Such drinks are therefore duty-free.

## Lower Means Dearer

Producers of alcohol-free and low-alcohol drinks benefit from the claw-back of revenue and then add to this cash advantage by charging more for them than for normal strength versions, claiming that the removal processes are expensive.

NABLABS are promoted by the big brewers for the reason that they are 'healthier' and that they are the ideal answer for

the worried driver. The latter may be true, but the brewers seem
to have a neat little profit-making scheme here, and by no
stretch of the imagination can drinks which contain so much
junk be considered 'healthier'.

When, early in 1989, BBC Television's *Food and Drink*
programme asked, via a general enquiry on CEEFAX, to hear
from viewers who had suffered hangover symptoms after
drinking NABLABS, twenty-seven people responded. Some
claimed they had experienced stomach disturbances, and others
reported severe headaches after drinking only a quart the night
before the hangover.

The BBC's enquiry (and the response it received) may have
been generated by the programme's drinks presenter, Jill
Goolden's having experienced hangover symptoms when
drinking NABLABS – a prime example of a subjective personal
reaction in search of elusive facts!

Dr Vic Garner, Lecturer in Chemistry at Manchester
Polytechnic, used a mass spectrometer to analyse samples of
NABLABS and discovered that, although the ethyl alcohol had
been removed by the brewer's process, the so-called 'congener
alcohol' isobutanol remained and that this alcohol may have
been responsible for the reported symptoms.

These hangover symptoms may be due to a synergistic
reaction following the removal of the ethyl alcohol, which is the
more drinker-friendly of the alcohols present. It could be that
aspartame or papain reacts with isobutanol remaining in the
drink. The most likely explanation is that these twenty-seven
people, who were described by a spokesman for the Brewers'
Society as an 'insignificant proportion' of the many NABLABS
drinkers in Britain, are allergic to the combination of additives
introduced into the drink after processing.

Regardless of the chemical complexity of NABLABS, their
most dangerous aspect is related to misleading labelling. Many
wines labelled 'low-alcohol' contain as much as 4 to 6 per cent
ABV, the same strength as a full-strength beer or cider, although
they are not drunk in volume as are beers and ciders.

EEC guidelines on accurate labelling of NABLABS are being
considered, but the British government's record of delay,
through derogation, means that the risk (especially to car
drivers) may continue for several years after they are issued.

## Century-old Ale Matures Rapidly

A little over a hundred years ago, somebody created a drink with a modern character – Cox's Anti-Burton, a non-fermented, no-alcohol bitter ale, produced in 1888.

This, the first of the NABLABS, was launched by the Temperance Movement as a weapon against the 'evils' of drink, because beer-drinkers could quench their thirst with it but avoid the typical undesirable effects of alcohol. These effects were perceived by the Movement as social rather than personal, and that perception was based upon widespread drunkenness and rowdyism in the streets. This in turn had been triggered by the government itself, in the shape of the Duke of Wellington's Beer Houses Act of 1830, which permitted any householder who could raise a £2 fee to open a house selling beer only.

No less than 15,000 beer-houses opened within the space of a month in Liverpool as a result of the new Act. The theory was that, with more beer available, the consumption of gin, which was very cheap, would fall, but since the beer-houses were unlicensed for wine and spirits, they were outside magisterial control. The only way to regain judicial control and thereby to limit drunkenness and rioting among a general public disenchanted with the astronomical price of bread was to re-license them for spirits. The result was a surge in both beer- and spirit-drinking, with convenient increases in revenue to the Exchequer. The Iron Duke had shifted from military strategy to fiscal manœuvres, with the populace as the pawn-like flags on his map of Britain. To add to the revenue rake-off, both malt and hops were further taxed.

Needless to remark, Cox's Anti-Burton was not a great success and was soon discontinued, and the gin-maker's anthem took over again: 'Drunk for a penny, dead drunk for tuppence.'

As well as being generally ignored by the drinkers of the time, Cox's 'NABLAB' served to unite the brewers against the Temperance Movement. Led by the new brewers at Burton-on-Trent, they set up the Licensed Victuallers National Defence League. Bass and Co, today Britain's largest brewers, led the campaign, with Michael Thomas Bass II, his brother Hamer and Michael's son Arthur all being elected to parliament on the anti-Temperance platform. This may or may not have reflected the opinion of the drinking public, most of whom were not eligible to vote. Numerous comments in newspapers also bore witness to the growing power of the brewers' lobby, many objecting to the 'preaching' tone of the temperance promoters.

An important factor in the popularity of beer was that, unlike the many dubious or thoroughly infected water supplies, beer had been boiled and was therefore 'safe' to drink. Beer-drinkers' decisions were therefore practical rather than moral or religious.

In modern times, the Temperance Movement has been replaced by groups such as Alcohol Concern and by the continuing effort of the Salvation Army. Most difficult to swallow for many drinkers are the anti-booze television 'specials' and six- or thirteen-week series. These often feature 'big stars', all proclaiming a sensible view of alcohol but being identified in the drinker's mind as members of the Temperance Movement in modern guise. This kind of message is often seen, rightly or wrongly, as identical in spirit (!) to that purveyed by numerous 'religion salesmen' who, sporting identifiably respectable suits and ties, harangue citizens about Sin and Salvation on their own doorsteps. As with the Temperance Movement, which claimed to encourage temperate (cautious) drinking but generally embraced abolitionism, many drinkers now interpret both the message from the media and that from Alcohol Concern as 'preaching' to the (by definition) sinful drinker.

The reaction, as with Cox's Anti-Burton and the Beer Houses Act, has been a steady increase in drinking, perhaps in defiance of the Temperance message. The reality is that people like to drink alcohol, and the way to guide them into healthier drinking lifestyles is by reaching a compromise which does not involve healthier-than-thou attitudes but offers realistic advice on alternative behaviour and alternative drinks.

The fact that most modern NABLABS are so chemically complicated should direct the drinker's attention to them. Quite clearly, they are the only acceptable answers for those who drive a car* and who like the taste of beer, wine or cider, but they must be approached with caution in view of their sometimes strange reported effects. Clausthaler and several supermarket 'own brands' are said to be additive-free.

Once again, a certain moderation is called for. As in all aspects

---

* With some exceptions. See p.76.

of human diet, nothing should be consumed in large quantities
– common table salt can kill if taken in sufficient amounts, for
example.

## Introduction to the Surveys

A few years ago Egon Ronay evoked the wrath of the British
motorway service-area staffs by attacking the quality of their
food and drink.

His reviewer's opinion may not have jeopardized advertising
revenue for his food guides, because motorway service-area
restaurants seldom advertise in such publications, but it raises a
question which is vital for the enquiring consumer. Can any
guide to taste or quality offer anything more than a rough
indication of standards, bearing in mind that reviewers'
opinions of quality vary so widely?

Hungry or thirsty motorway drivers are captive in respect of
the range of choice available (unless they leave the motorway
and plough through slow-moving traffic to a little town bistro!),
but the drinker or diner often finds that the 'superb quality' or
'highly recommended' conclusions of food, wine and beer
guides fail to live up to expectations when the pub or restaurant
is visited. Damning opinions often seem equally wide of the
mark.

For most reviewers, however (those who have at heart the
continued flow of advertising revenue to their publication),
wines are 'fruity', 'fresh-tasting', 'full-bodied' or 'well-balanced',
while beers are invariably 'well-hopped', 'refreshing' or 'malty'.

With these lessons in mind, I have dealt with the matter of
offering commercial guides to alternative drinks (alternatives to
additive-laden examples) with an 'information only' approach,
dispensing with my own views about which of the wines or
beers tastes best. Such opinions (which are no better than mine!)
are available from many sources, such as Hugh Johnson's *Pocket
Wine Book*, Michael Jackson's *International Beer Guide*, *The Good
Beer Guide*, *The Good Cider Guide* and *The Organic Wine Guide*,
which lists new ranges of wines as they become available.
National newspapers also provide 'tastings' material, such as
the *Daily Telegraph*'s Saturday guide to food and drink. All such
opinions are highly personal.

In order to eliminate any misleading responses from the

brewers in the surveys which follow, I visited many of the
breweries listed and was permitted to check materials in use
(and in store) at those included in *The Pure Beer Brewers*. All
those others who responded with information did so in
considerable detail.

Public houses, bars and hotels supplying beers from the
breweries listed here can be identified in *The Good Beer Guide*.

## Survey 1: The Pure Beer Brewers

Unlike many wine- and spirits-producers, some commercial
brewers in Britain, especially the small one- and two-man
businesses and the so-called 'independents' (larger concerns
who have no direct links with the big eight combines), are
prepared to give information on their use of materials and/or
additives.

From all Britain's breweries (a total of 208) which I contacted,
only eighteen can be said to be producing additive-free beer. In
each case, these pure-beer brewers agreed that their methods
and breweries are open to public view (by appointment, in order
not to disturb brewing-schedules), stressing that they have
'nothing to hide'. Between them they brew sixty different beers.

These breweries are listed below, as are two further breweries
(Fuller's and Young's) where lager is brewed to an additive-free
standard. Each brewery listed is given with its named beers,
relevant original gravities* (given at the mid-point of the range)
and an equivalent rough approximation of alcohol by volume.

None of the Big Eight breweries is represented here. With the
exception of the two national-brand lagers referred to, and two
small brewery lagers, all the beers shown are real ales. Only one
bottled beer is listed.

* See Glossary

KEY: (I) independent brewery
(HB) home-brew pub

**BALLARD'S BREWERY LTD**, Unit C, The Old Sawmills, Nyewood, Rogate, Petersfield, Hants (I)

| *Beers*: | | | |
|---|---|---|---|
| | Trotton Bitter | (1,036) | 4.0 per cent |
| | Ballard's Best Bitter | (1,042) | 5.0 per cent |
| | Ballard's Wassail | (1,060) | 7.0 per cent |

**BANKS AND TAYLOR**, The Brewery, Shefford, Beds (I). Not to be confused with Bank's of Wolverhampton.

| *Beers*: | | | |
|---|---|---|---|
| | Shefford Bitter | (1,038) | 4.4 per cent |
| | Eastcote SPA (or Eastcote (Ale) | (1,041) | 4.8 per cent |
| | SOS (Shefford Old Strong) | (1,050) | 6.0 per cent |
| | SOD (Shefford Old Dark | (1,055) | 6.8 per cent |
| | Wembley Wobbly (or Two XS, i.e. 'to excess') | (1,060) | 7.0 per cent (occasional brew) |

**BERROW BREWERY**, Coast Road, Berrow, Burnham-on-Sea, Somerset (I)

| *Beers*: | | | |
|---|---|---|---|
| | Berrow BBBB | (1,038) | 4.4 per cent |
| | Topsy Turvy | (1,050) | 6.0 per cent |

**BLACKAWTON BREWERY**, Washbourne, Totnes, Devon (I)

| *Beers*: | | | | |
|---|---|---|---|---|
| | Blackawton Bitter | (1,037) | 4.2 per cent | (R) |
| | Devon Gold | (1,040) | 4.6 per cent | (R) |
| | Forty-Four | (1,044) | 5.4 per cent | (R) |
| | Headstrong | (1,049) | 6.0 per cent | (R) |

**BLUE ANCHOR**, Helston, Cornwall (HB)

| *Beers*: | | | | |
|---|---|---|---|---|
| | Medium | (1,050) | 6.0 per cent | (R) |
| | Best Bitter | (1,053) | 6.5 per cent | (R) |
| | Special | (1,066) | 7.5 per cent | (R) |
| | Extra Special | (1,070) | 8.0 per cent | (R) |

**BUNCE'S BREWERY**, The Old Mill, Mill Road, Netheravon, Wilts (I)

| *Beers*: | | | |
|---|---|---|---|
| | Benchmark | (1,035) | 4.0 per cent |
| | Best Bitter | (1,042) | 4.8 per cent |
| | Old Smokey | (1,050) | 6.0 per cent |

**CHILTERN BREWERY**, Nash Lee Road, Terrick, Aylesbury, Bucks (I)

| *Beers*: | | | |
|---|---|---|---|
| | Chiltern Ale | (1,036) | 4.0 per cent |
| | Beechwood Bitter | (1,043) | 5.0 per cent |
| | Three Hundreds Old Ale | (1,050) | 6.0 per cent (on draught in winter, but bottled, naturally conditioned, otherwise) |

DONNINGTON BREWERY, Stow-on-the-Wold, Glos (I)

| Beers: | Donnington XXX | (1,035) | 4.0 per cent |
|---|---|---|---|
| | Donnington BB | (1,036) | 4.0 per cent |
| | Donnington SBA | (1,042) | 5.0 per cent |

FULLER, SMITH & TURNER plc, Griffin Brewery, Chiswick, London W4 (I)

| Beers: | Fuller's K2 Lager | (1,040) | 4.6 per cent |
|---|---|---|---|

GLENNY BREWERY CO, Two Rivers Brewery, Station Lane, Witney, Oxon (I)

| Beers: | Witney Bitter | (1,037) | 4.2 per cent |
|---|---|---|---|
| | Wychwood Best | (1,044) | 5.4 per cent |
| | Hobgoblin | (1,058) | 6.5 per cent |

MILL BREWERY, Unit 18c, Bradley Lane, Newton, Devon (I)

| Beers: | Janner's Ale | (1,038) | 4.4 per cent |
|---|---|---|---|
| | Devon Special | (1,045) | 5.2 per cent |
| | Christmas Ale | (1,050) | 5.8 per cent |

MINER'S ARMS BREWERY, Westbury-sub-Mendip, Somerset (I)

| Beers: | Own Ale | (1,040) | 4.6 per cent |
|---|---|---|---|
| | Guvnor's Special Brew | (1,048) | 5.4 per cent |

OLD MILL BREWERY, Mill Street, Snaith, Goole, Humberside (I)

| Beers: | Old Mill Traditional Mild | (1,034) | 4.0 per cent |
|---|---|---|---|
| | Alt Mühle Lager | (1,034) | 4.0 per cent |
| | Old Mill Traditional Bitter | (1,037) | 4.2 per cent |
| | Bullion Bitter | (1,044) | 5.4 per cent |

PLASSEY BREWERY, Eyton, Wrexham, Clwyd (I)

| Beers: | Farmhouse Bitter | (1,038) | 4.2 per cent |
|---|---|---|---|

POWELL BREWERY, Mochdre Industrial Estate, Newtown, Powys (I)

| Beers: | Sam Powell Best Bitter | (1,035) | 4.0 per cent |
|---|---|---|---|
| | Sam Powell Original Bitter | (1,038) | 4.4 per cent |
| | Old Sam | (1,050) | 5.6 per cent |

THOMPSON'S BREWERY, London Inn, 11 West Street, Ashburton, Devon (I)

| Beers: | Thompson's Mild | (1,033) | 3.8 per cent |
|---|---|---|---|
| | Thompson's Lager | (1,036) | 4.2 per cent |
| | Dartmoor Bitter | (1,037) | 4.2 per cent |
| | Thompson's Bitter | (1,040) | 4.6 per cent |
| | Thompson's IPA | (1,045) | 5.5 per cent |
| | Christmas Tipple | (1,050) | 6.0 per cent |

THREE TUNS BREWERY, Bishop's Castle, Salop (HB)

| *Beers:* | | | |
|---|---|---|---|
| | Mild | (1,035) | 4.0 per cent |
| | XXX | (1,042) | 5.2 per cent |
| | Castle Steamer | (1,045) | 5.4 per cent |
| | Old Scrooge | (1,054) | 6.0 per cent |
| | | | (Christmas brew) |

ULEY BREWERY, The Old Brewery, 31 The Street, Uley, Dursley, Glos (I)

| *Beers:* | | | |
|---|---|---|---|
| | Hogshead (or UB40) | (1,037) | 4.4 per cent |
| | Uley Bitter | (1,040) | 4.6 per cent |
| | Old Spot | (1,050) | 5.6 per cent |
| | Pig's Ear | (1,050) | 6.0 per cent |
| | Pigor Mortis | (1,058) | 7.0 per cent |

WOOD'S BREWERY, Wistanstow, Craven Arms, Salop (I) (HB)

| *Beers:* | | | |
|---|---|---|---|
| | Parish Bitter | (1,040) | 4.6 per cent |
| | Wood's Special | (1,043) | 5.2 per cent |
| | Wood's Wonderful | (1,050) | 6.0 per cent |
| | Christmas Cracker | (1,060) | 7.0 per cent |
| | | | (Christmas brew) |

YOUNG'S RAM BREWERY, High Street, Wandsworth, London SW18 (I)

| *Beers:* | | | |
|---|---|---|---|
| | Young's Premium Lager | (1,047) | 5.8 per cent |

## Survey 2: The Near-Pure Beer Brewers

Fewer than ten additives are used at each of the breweries listed below. In every case, brewers are prepared to 'brew and tell' about their use of additives, which are given with their E prefix numbers where appropriate. Between them, these brewers produce 165 different beers, most of them available nationally.

KEY: (7B) affiliated to or wholly owned by one of the Big Eight brewing combines
(I) independent brewery
(HB) home-brew pub
(KB) keg bitter
(KL) keg lager } Beer type abbreviations,
(KM) keg mild } see Basic Beer Types, p. 72
(KS) keg stout
(R) real ale

BASS, Wellpark Brewery, Duke Street, Glasgow (7B). Bass is Britain's largest brewer.

| *Beers:* | | | | |
|---|---|---|---|---|
| | Tennents Pilsner | (1,035) | 4.0 per cent | (KL) |

|                    |          |              |      |
|--------------------|----------|--------------|------|
| Carling Black Label | (1,037) | 4.2 per cent | (KL) |
| Tennents Lager      | (1,038) | 4.4 per cent | (KL) |
| Tennents Export     | (1,042) | 5.0 per cent | (KL) |
| Tennents Extra      | (1,044) | 5.4 per cent | (KL) |

*Additives*: E150(c) ammonia caramel
E405 propylene glycol alginate
516 calcium sulphate
518 magnesium sulphate

BATHAM'S, Delph Brewery, Brierley Hill, West Midlands (I)

| *Beers*: | Batham's Mild | (1,036) | 4.0 per cent | (R) |
|----------|---------------|---------|--------------|-----|
|          | Batham's Bitter | (1,043) | 5.2 per cent | (R) |
|          | Delph Strong Ale | (1,054) | 6.0 per cent | (R) |
|          | (Christmas brew) |       |              |     |

*Additives*: E220 sulphur dioxide

BEAMISH & CRAWFORD, South Main Street, Cork, Eire. Owned by Canadian brewers Carling O'Keefe.

| *Beers*: | Beamish Stout | (1,039) | 4.5 per cent | (KS) |
|----------|---------------|---------|--------------|------|
|          | Carling Black Label | (1,037) | 4.2 per cent | (KL) |

*Additives*: E150(c) ammonia caramel (used only in stout)
E220 sulphur dioxide
E338 phosphoric acid
E405 propylene glycol alginate
516 calcium sulphate

BERKHAMSTEAD BREWERY, Bourne End Lane, Bourne End, Herts (I)

| *Beers*: | Berkhamstead Best Bitter | (1,041) | 4.8 per cent | (R) |
|----------|--------------------------|---------|--------------|-----|
|          | Christmas Special | (1,055) | 7.0 per cent | (R) |
|          | Premium | (1,055) | 6.2 per cent | (R) |

*Additives*: 513 sulphuric acid
516 calcium sulphate

BIG LAMP BREWERY, Summer Hill Street, Newcastle-upon-Tyne (I)

| *Beers*: | Big Lamp Bitter | (1,038) | 4.2 per cent | (R) |
|----------|-----------------|---------|--------------|-----|
|          | Stout | (1,044) | 5.2 per cent | (R) |
|          | Prince Bishop's Ale | (1,044) | 5.2 per cent | (R) |
|          | Old Genie | (1,070) | 8.5 per cent | (R) |
|          | Blackout | (1,100) | 13.5 per cent | (R) |

*Additives*: 516 calcium sulphate

BROADLAND BREWERY, WOODBASTICK, Norwich (I)

| *Beers*: | Broadsman | (1,036) | 4.0 per cent | (R) |
|----------|-----------|---------|--------------|-----|
|          | Wherry Best Bitter | (1,039) | 4.5 per cent | (R) |
|          | Norfolk Porter | (1,041) | 4.8 per cent | (R) |
|          | Old Bram | (1,045) | 5.4 per cent | (R) |
|          | Phoenix XXX | (1,047) | 5.6 per cent | (R) |
|          | Head Cracker | (1,069) | 7.8 per cent | (R) |

**MATTHEW BROWN, PO Box 5, Lion Brewery, Blackburn, Lancs (7B – Scottish & Newcastle Breweries)**

| *Beers*: | | | | |
|---|---|---|---|---|
| | Mild | (1,031) | 3.5 per cent | (R and KB) |
| | Light | (1,033) | 3.8 per cent | (KB) |
| | Bitter | (1,036) | 4.0 per cent | (R and KB) |
| | Slalom Lager | (1,036) | 4.0 per cent | (KL) |
| | Slalom D Lager | (1,045) | 5.5 per cent | (KL) |

*Additives*: E150(c) ammonia caramel
E222 sodium hydrogen sulphite
E401 sodium alginate
516 calcium sulphate
518 magnesium sulphate
551 silicon dioxide
558 bentonite

**BURTON BRIDGE BREWERY, Bridge Street, Burton-on-Trent, Staffs (I)**

| *Beers*: | | | | |
|---|---|---|---|---|
| | XL Bitter | (1,040) | 4.6 per cent | (R) |
| | Bridge Bitter | (1,042) | 5.0 per cent | (R) |
| | Burton Porter | (1,045) | 5.2 per cent | (R) |
| | Top Dog Stout | (1,050) | 5.6 per cent | (R) |
| | Burton Festival Ale | (1,055) | 6.0 per cent | (R) |
| | Old Expensive | (1,066) | 7.5 per cent | (R) |

*Additives*: E150(c) ammonia caramel – 'used occasionally'
E220 sulphur dioxide – present in isinglass finings
E338 phosphoric acid – for acid-washing of yeast (see Glossary)

**BURTONWOOD BREWERY plc, Bold Lane, Burtonwood, Warrington, Ches (I)**

| *Beers*: | | | | |
|---|---|---|---|---|
| | Burtonwood Dark Mild | (1,032) | 3.5 per cent | (R) |
| | Burtonwood Bitter | (1,036) | 4.0 per cent | (R) |

*Additives*: E150(c) ammonia caramel
E220 sulphur dioxide
E300 ascorbic acid
513 sulphuric acid
516 calcium sulphate

**CALEDONIAN BREWERY, Slateford Road, Edinburgh (I)**

| *Beers*: | | | | |
|---|---|---|---|---|
| | Best Scotch (or 70/- Ale) | (1,036) | 4.0 per cent | (R) |
| | Porter | (1,036) | 4.0 per cent | (R) |
| | 80/- Ale | (1,043) | 5.0 per cent | (R) |
| | Merman XXX | (1,052) | 5.8 per cent | (R) |
| | Strong Ale | (1,080) | 9.5 per cent | (R) |

*Additives*: 516 calcium sulphate
518 magnesium sulphate

**CLIFTON INNS LTD, The Orange Brewery, Pimlico Road, London SW1 (7B – Watney) One of a chain of home-brew pubs.**

| *Beers*: | | | | |
|---|---|---|---|---|
| | Pimlico Light | (1,036) | 4.0 per cent | (R) |
| | SW1 | (1,040) | 4.6 per cent | (R) |

|  |  |  |  |
|---|---|---|---|
| Pimlico Porter | (1,046) | 5.3 per cent | (R) |
| SW2 | (1,050) | 5.6 per cent | (R) |

*Additives*: 513 sulphuric acid
516 calcium sulphate

**COTLEIGH BREWERY, Ford Road, Wiveliscombe, Somerset (I)**

| *Beers*: |  |  |  |  |
|---|---|---|---|---|
|  | Harrier Spa | (1,036) | 4.0 per cent | (R) |
|  | Tawny Bitter | (1,040) | 4.6 per cent | (R) |
|  | Old Buzzard | (1,048) | 5.6 per cent | (R) |

*Additives*: 516 calcium sulphate

**FELINFOEL BREWERY, Felinfoel, Llanelli, Dyfed (I)**

| *Beers*: |  |  |  |  |
|---|---|---|---|---|
|  | Felinfoel Mild | (1,031) | 3.3 per cent | (R) |
|  | Bitter Ale | (1,034) | 3.8 per cent | (R) |
|  | Felinfoel Bitter | (1,034) | 3.8 per cent | (R) |
|  | Double Dragon | (1,040) | 4.6 per cent | (R) |

*Additives*: E222 sodium hydrogen sulphite
E405 propylene glycol alginate
524 sodium hydroxide
551 silicon dioxide

**FULLER SMITH & TURNER, plc, Griffin Brewery, Chiswick, London W4 (I)**

| *Beers*: |  |  |  |  |
|---|---|---|---|---|
|  | Chiswick Bitter | (1,035.5) | 3.8 per cent | (R) |
|  | Fuller's Mild | (1,035.5) | 3.8 per cent | (R) |
|  | Fuller's Bitter | (1,035.5) | 3.8 per cent | (R) |
|  | London Pride | (1,041.5) | 5.0 per cent | (R) |
|  | Extra Special Bitter (ESB) | (1,055.75) | 6.1 per cent | (R) |

*Additives*: E150(c) ammonia caramel
E222 sodium hydrogen sulphite
516 calcium sulphate
Note: Flaked maize is an ingredient of Fuller's ales.

**GOACHER'S BREWERY, Hayle Mill Cottages, Bockingford, Maidstone, Kent (I)**

| *Beers*: |  |  |  |  |
|---|---|---|---|---|
|  | Maidstone Light | (1,036) | 4.0 per cent | (R) |
|  | Dark Maidstone Ale | (1,040) | 4.6 per cent | (R) |
|  | Old Maidstone Ale | (1,066) | 7.3 per cent | (R) |

*Additives*: E220 sulphur dioxide
516 calcium sulphate
518 magnesium sulphate

**GREENALL WHITLEY, Wilderspool Brewery, PO Box 2, Warrington, Ches (7B). The 'youngest' of the Big Eight breweries.**

| *Beers*: |  |  |  |  |
|---|---|---|---|---|
|  | Haagen Lager | (1,032) | 3.3 per cent | (KL) |
|  | Shipstone's Mild | (1,034) | 3.5 per cent | (R and KB) |
|  | Grünhalle Lager | (1,035) | 3.8 per cent | (KL) |
|  | Greenall Whitley Mild | (1,035) | 3.8 per cent | (R and KB) |
|  | Davenport's Mild | (1,035.1) | 3.8 per cent | (R and KB) |
|  | Local Bitter | (1,036.5) | 3.9 per cent | (R) |

|                      |                        |               |      |
|----------------------|------------------------|---------------|------|
| WEM Best Bitter      | (1,037.5) 4.1 per cent | (R)           |      |
| Shipstone's Bitter   | (1,037.7) 4.2 per cent | (R)           |      |
| Davenport's Bitter   | (1,038.9) 4.2 per cent | (R)           |      |
| WEM Special Bitter   | (1,042.5) 5.2 per cent | (R)           |      |
| Grünhalle Export     | (1,045)   5.4 per cent | (KL)          |      |

*Additives*: E150(c) ammonia caramel – used only in dark ales
E220 sulphur dioxide
516 calcium sulphate

Note: Grünhalle Lager and Grünhalle Export are brewed under licence from Randall's Vautier of Jersey.

GUERNSEY BREWERY, South Esplanade, St Peter Port, Guernsey (I). This brewery trades under the name Pony Ales.

| *Beers*:       |                |                        |      |
|----------------|----------------|------------------------|------|
|                | LBA Mild       | (1,037.5) 4.1 per cent | (R)  |
|                | Draught Bitter | (1,045)   5.5 per cent | (R)  |

*Additives*: Natural caramel (no E prefix necessary)
E220 sulphur dioxide
E300 ascorbic acid
516 calcium sulphate
518 magnesium sulphate

Note: In Guernsey, Excise Duty is levied on beer quantity generated and not upon alcohol-content.

GUINNESS BREWING, Arthur Guinness & Son (Great Britain) Ltd, Park Royal Brewery, London NW10 (7B)

| *Beers*:       |                                |           |             |      |
|----------------|--------------------------------|-----------|-------------|------|
|                | Harp Lager                     | (1,032)   | 3.3 per cent | (KL) |
|                | Draught Guinness               | (1,038)   | 4.1 per cent | (KS) |
|                | Harp Special (or Harp Extra)   | (1,041)   | 4.8 per cent | (KL) |

*Additives*: E300 ascorbic acid
E401 sodium alginate
E405 propylene glycol alginate
558 bentonite

Note: The Park Royal brewery also produces one of the most famous bottled beers in the world – Guinness Extra Stout (1,042) 5.0 per cent. This is a naturally conditioned stout. See Glossary.

HALL & WOODHOUSE, Blandford Forum, Dorset (I)

| *Beers*:       |                    |           |             |      |
|----------------|--------------------|-----------|-------------|------|
|                | Brock Lager        | (1,033)   | 3.4 per cent | (KL) |
|                | Malthouse          | (1,033)   | 3.4 per cent | (KB) |
|                | Hector's Bitter    | (1,034)   | 3.5 per cent | (R)  |
|                | Badger Export      | (1,037)   | 4.0 per cent | (KB) |
|                | Badger Best Bitter | (1,041)   | 4.8 per cent | (R)  |
|                | Hofbräu Export     | (1,042)   | 5.0 per cent | (KL) |
|                | Royal Hofbräu      | (1,047)   | 5.3 per cent | (KL) |
|                | Tanglefoot         | (1,048)   | 5.4 per cent | (R)  |

*Additives*: E150(c) ammonia caramel
E222 sodium hydrogen sulphite
E405 propylene glycol alginate

**HOLDEN'S BREWERY**, George Street, Woodsetton, Dudley, West Midlands (I)

| Beers: | | | | |
|---|---|---|---|---|
| | Holden's Stout | (1,034) | 4.0 per cent | (R) |
| | Holden's Mild | (1,036) | 4.0 per cent | (R) |
| | Holden's Bitter | (1,038) | 4.2 per cent | (R) |
| | Holden's XB | (1,042) | 4.8 per cent | (R) |
| | Holden's Special Bitter | (1,050) | 5.6 per cent | (R) |
| | Old Ale | (1,080) | 9.2 per cent | (R) |

*Additives*: E220 sulphur dioxide
516 calcium sulphate

**KING & BARNES**, 18 Bishopric, Horsham, West Sussex (I)

| Beers: | | | | |
|---|---|---|---|---|
| | Sussex Mild | (1,034) | 3.5 per cent | (R) |
| | Sussex Bitter | (1,034) | 3.5 per cent | (R) |
| | JK Lager | (1,036) | 4.0 per cent | (KL) |
| | Old Ale | (1,046) | 5.5 per cent | (R) |
| | Draught Festive | (1,050) | 5.8 per cent | (R) |

*Additives*: E150(c) ammonia caramel
E300 ascorbic acid

**MALTON BREWERY**, Crown Hotel, Wheelgate, Malton, North Yorks (I)

| Beers: | | | | |
|---|---|---|---|---|
| | Malton Pale Ale | (1,033) | 3.4 per cent | (R) |
| | Double Chance | (1,038) | 4.4 per cent | (R) |
| | Pickwick's Porter | (1,041.8) | 4.8 per cent | (R) |
| | Owd Bob | (1,054) | 6.2 per cent | (R) |

*Additives*: 516 calcium sulphate
518 magnesium sulphate

**MARTIN ALES**, Martin Hall, Martin, Dover, Kent (I)

| Beers: | | | | |
|---|---|---|---|---|
| | Johnson's Bitter | (1,042) | 5.0 per cent | (R) |
| | College Ale | (1,080) | 9.5 per cent | (R) |

*Additives*: E338 phosphoric acid

**MITCHELLS OF LANCASTER**, Moor Lane, Manchester (I)

| Beers: | | | | |
|---|---|---|---|---|
| | Mitchell's Mild | (1,035) | 4.0 per cent | (R) |
| | Mitchell's Bitter | (1,036) | 4.0 per cent | (R) |
| | Mitchell's ESB | (1,045) | 5.2 per cent | (R) |

*Additives*: 516 calcium sulphate

**MORLAND**, PO Box 5, Ock Street, Abingdon, Oxon (I)

| Beers: | | | | |
|---|---|---|---|---|
| | Morland Mild | (1,032) | 3.5 per cent | (R) |
| | Morland Bitter | (1,035) | 4.0 per cent | (R) |
| | Old Masters (formerly | | | |
| | Best Bitter) | (1,041) | 4.8 per cent | (R) |
| | Artists Keg | (1,032) | 3.5 per cent | (KB) |

*Additives*: E220 sulphur dioxide (in isinglass finings)
516 calcium sulphate

**MORRELL'S BREWERY**, Lion Brewery, St Thomas Street, Oxford (I)

| *Beers*: | | | | |
|---|---|---|---|---|
| | Light Ale | (1,032) | 3.3 per cent | (R) |
| | Pale Ale | (1,032) | 3.3 per cent | (KB) |
| | Morrell's Bitter | (1,036) | 4.0 per cent | (R) |
| | Friar's Ale | (1,036) | 4.0 per cent | (KB) |
| | Varsity | (1,041) | 4.8 per cent | (R and KB) |
| | Celebration | (1,066) | 7.5 per cent | (R) |
| | College | (1,072) | 8.0 per cent | (R) |

*Additives*: E150(c) ammonia caramel – only in mild ale
516 calcium sulphate

**MURPHY'S**, Ladyswell Brewery, Cork, Eire (I). This brewery is a subsidiary of Heineken of the Netherlands.

| *Beers*: | | | | |
|---|---|---|---|---|
| | Murphy's Stout | (1,038) | 4.4 per cent | (KS) |

*Additives*: E220 sulphur dioxide
E405 propylene glycol alginate
513 sulphuric acid
516 calcium sulphate

**NETHERGATE BREWERY CO LTD**, 11–13 High Street, Clare, Suffolk (I)

| *Beers*: | | | | |
|---|---|---|---|---|
| | Nethergate Bitter | (1,039) | 4.6 per cent | (R) |
| | Old Growler | (1,055) | 6.2 per cent | (R) |

*Additives*: E338 phosphoric acid – both additives used for acid-washing of yeast. See Glossary.
500 sodium carbonate

**OAK BREWERY**, Merseyton Road, Ellesmere Port, Ches (I)

| *Beers*: | | | | |
|---|---|---|---|---|
| | Oak Best Bitter | (1,038) | 4.4 per cent | (R) |
| | Old Oak Ale | (1,044) | 5.4 per cent | (R) |
| | Double Dagger | (1,050) | 5.6 per cent | (R) |
| | Porter | (1,050) | 5.6 per cent | (R) |
| | Wobbly Bob | (1,060) | 7.0 per cent | (R) |

*Additives*: 516 calcium sulphate

**OAKHILL, OLD BREWERY**, High Street, Oakhill, Bath, Avon (I)

| *Beers*: | | | | |
|---|---|---|---|---|
| | Oakhill Bitter | (1,038) | 4.4 per cent | (R) |
| | Yeoman Ale | (1,048) | 5.0 per cent | (R) |

*Additives*: E220 sulphur dioxide
516 calcium sulphate
518 magnesium sulphate

**PLYMPTON BREWERY**, Valley Road, Plympton, Plymouth, Devon (7B – Allied Breweries)

| *Beers*: | | | | |
|---|---|---|---|---|
| | Plympton Best | (1,039) | 4.6 per cent | (R) |
| | Dartmoor Strong | (1,045) | 5.5 per cent | (R) |

*Additives*: 516 calcium sulphate

RANDALL'S VAUTIER, PO Box 43, Clare Street, St Helier, Jersey (I)
*Beers*:       Local Bitter            (1,036)   4.0 per cent   (KB)
               Grünhalle Lager         (1,038)   4.4 per cent   (KL)
               Top Island              (1,043)   5.2 per cent   (KB)
               Export Gold             (1,045)   5.5 per cent   (KL)
*Additives*: E220 sulphur dioxide
             516 calcium sulphate


RIDLEY'S BREWERY, Hartford End, Chelmsford, Essex (I)
*Beers*:       Ridley's XXXX           (1,034)   3.5 per cent   (R)
               Ridley's PA             (1,034)   3.5 per cent   (R)
               Ridley's HE             (1,045)   5.5 per cent   (R)
               Bishop's                (1,080)   9.2 per cent   (R)
*Additives*: E150(c) ammonia caramel – dark beers only
             E220 sulphur dioxide
             E401 sodium alginate
             E405 propylene glycol alginate
             516 calcium sulphate

RINGWOOD BREWERY, 138 Christchurch Road, Ringwood, Hants (I)
*Beers*:       Ringwood Best Bitter    (1,040)   4.6 per cent   (R)
               Fortyniner              (1,049)   5.4 per cent   (R)
               Ringwood 4X             (1,049)   5.4 per cent   (R)
               Old Thumper             (1,060)   7.0 per cent   (R)
*Additives*: 516 calcium sulphate


RUDDLES BREWERY, Langham, Oakham, Rutland, Leics (7B – Watney)
*Beers*:       Best Bitter (formerly
                 Rutland Bitter)       (1,037)   4.2 per cent   (R)
               Ruddles County          (1,050)   5.6 per cent   (R)
*Additives*: E300 ascorbic acid
             E338 phosphoric acid
             513 sulphuric acid
             516 calcium sulphate


SHEPHERD NEAME, 17 Court Street, Faversham, Kent (I)
*Beers*:       Master Brew Mild        (1,031)   3.2 per cent   (KB)
               Master Brew XX          (1,033)   3.5 per cent   (KB)
               Steinbock Lager         (1,034)   4.0 per cent   (KL)
               Master Brew Bitter      (1,036)   4.0 per cent   (R)
               Abbey                   (1,039)   4.5 per cent   (KB)
               Hurlimann Sternbräu     (1,045)   5.5 per cent   (KL)
               Bishop's Finger         (1,048)   5.8 per cent   (R)
*Additives*: E220 sulphur dioxide
             516 calcium sulphate
             518 magnesium sulphate

VAUX BREWERIES, Sunderland, Tyne and Wear (I)

| *Beers*: | | | | |
|---|---|---|---|---|
| | Tuborg Lager | (1,030) | 3.2 per cent | (KL) |
| | Frisk Lager | (1,033) | 3.5 per cent | (KL) |
| | Original Pale | (1,033) | 3.5 per cent | (KB) |
| | Vaux Mild | (1,033) | 3.5 per cent | (KM) |
| | Sunderland Draught | (1,040) | 4.6 per cent | (KB) |
| | Samson | (1,042) | 5.0 per cent | (KB) |
| | Vaux Regal | (1,044) | 5.4 per cent | (KL) |

*Additives*: 516 calcium sulphate
518 magnesium sulphate

WYE VALLEY BREWERY, 69 St Owen's Street, Hereford (I)

| *Beers*: | | | | |
|---|---|---|---|---|
| | Hereford Bitter | (1,038) | 4.4 per cent | (R) |
| | HPA | (1,040) | 4.5 per cent | (R) |
| | Hereford Supreme | (1,043) | 5.2 per cent | (R) |
| | Brew 69 | (1,055) | 6.2 per cent | (R) |

*Additives*: 518 magnesium sulphate

YOUNGS, Ram Brewery, High Street, Wandsworth, London SW18 (I)

| *Beers*: | | | | |
|---|---|---|---|---|
| | Tuborg Lager | (1,030) | 3.2 per cent | (KL) |
| | Young's Bitter | (1,036) | 3.2 per cent | (KL) |
| | London Lager | (1,037) | 4.2 per cent | (KL) |
| | Young's Special | (1,046) | 5.6 per cent | (R) |
| | Winter Warmer | (1,055) | 6.0 per cent | (R) |

*Additives*: E150(c) ammonia caramel
516 calcium sulphate

# 4   Cider

Cider and tinned salmon – the staple diet of the agricultural classes.
Evelyn Waugh, *Scoop*

## 'Ale' from the Apple

My paternal grandfather brewed his own cider. It was a deep golden colour and brain-numbingly strong. Much of the back garden of his home at Rowledge, on the Surrey/Hampshire border, was devoted to the paraphernalia connected with his hobby and thirst-quencher.

As a boy I helped him to gather apples from numerous gardens and orchards in and around the village, later assisting him in the crushing of the fruit in a home-made wooden device of massive proportions. Part of my duties – I was paid a penny a day – involved keeping wasps away from the crusher, although grandad's awesome technique at this vital task (dead wasps don't improve the cider) made me feel redundant. He would pick each insect off the crusher and quite deliberately squeeze it to death between finger and thumb. At the time I marvelled at his courage, but I can now see that his work as a jobbing gardener had produced leather-like skin on his fingers. The wasps didn't stand a chance.

My first taste of grandad's cider came when I was eleven. He brought a half-pint into the kitchen where I was getting a drink of water on a very hot autumn day.

'There's summat with a bit o' taste to it, young Ted,' he said.

Millie, my grannie, sprang to my physical and moral defence: 'Don't give the boy that poisonous muck, Arth,' she said. 'He'll get a headache, and his mother will know why.'

She added a liberal quantity of water, but I recall that it tasted good, slightly acrid, with the powerful aroma of fresh apples. The headache lasted the whole of the next day.

Grandad kept some 'special brew' cider in the woodshed. Occasionally I would see him filling a jug from a huge wooden

94

cask. This brew was much darker than his daily pint, and grandad would lapse into slumber in his battered leather-covered armchair within a few minutes of sinking a pint of it. The only materials used in his brews were apple juice, sugar and fresh air. Wild yeasts in the latter ingredient carried out the fermentation, aided by 'relatives' which remained on the apple skins.

Arch, my father, was also a practical man. He could repair just about anything mechanical or electrical and frequently did so for friends and relatives. He was a brilliant watchmaker but, as far as I know, he never turned his hand to brewing or winemaking, preferring to quaff the local brews at 'the club', which is where he introduced me to real ale and gassy cider, the big brewer's 'load o' chemicals', as grandad called it. The taste was probably no worse than the modern, watery version, but at the time I wondered how my stomach could contain such expanding quantities of gas.

Some years later I sampled the real thing again, straight from a Somerset farm. The taste brought back memories of Grandad Arth, by now long gone and his cider press rotted away.

Cider-making began in Spain in the Middle Ages, when it was also popular in England, spreading across the Channel via Normandy, France, where it remains a strong seller.

By the seventeenth century, the West Country had become a centre of cider-making, although the taste for it declined in the eighteenth century, when beer, and especially pale ale, came into vogue. A revival during the 1960s has been responsible for two 'arms' of the craft developing:

(1) industrial cider-making, using cultured champagne yeasts and modern techniques, producing keg cider. These national-brand ciders such as Gaymer's and Coates are owned by the large brewing combines.

(2) An extensive farm-based craft producing so-called 'scrumpy', a flavourful but cloudy and strong 'real ale' type cider, naturally conditioned and served straight from the cask on gravity.

The main problem about making decisions on scrumpy is that recipes vary from farm to farm and brewer to brewer (not all scrumpy comes from farms), so it is probably best to adopt a taste-and-see process, always remembering that scrumpy-drinking can be a recipe for a killer of a hangover. This is probably due to wild yeast activity, producing slightly more methanol or congener alcohols in the drink than are produced by a cultured yeast. Alcoholic strength of these real ciders varies between four and 8.5 per cent by volume, original gravity not being used as a measurement.

Where the draught keg cider in the pubs is concerned, a decision is easy, because they are all brewed with a cultured yeast, fined, filtered, pasteurized and carbonated before being cooled at the point of dispense – just like keg stouts, ales and lagers, but with a different flavour base. Ciders such as Strongbow, Gaymer's Olde English Strong Cyder and Taunton (also available as real cider in some pubs) are keg versions.

Sainsbury is the only British supermarket claiming to supply cider – its Medium Dry Cider (bottled) – in a form which contains 'no artificial preservatives'. Whether this drink is truly additive-free (it clearly contains alcohol, a 'natural preservative') is uncertain, since neither makers nor retailers are required to give details of ingredients, except for alcohol-content.

As for most processed ales and lagers, it is possible to construct a list of additives for keg ciders. These include:

E200 sorbic acid, which is used as a pH-adjuster (*see* Glossary) to balance the high tannin content of the best cider apples:

E220 sulphur dioxide – used as a preservative in the cask or bottle;

E222 sodium hydrogen sulphite – used as a preservative and cask-sterilizer;

E223 sodium metabisulphite – used to sterilize apple skins when a cultured yeast is used;

E226 calcium sulphite – used as a cask-sterilizer and anti-bacterial agent;

E300 L-ascorbic acid – used as an anti-oxidant in keg draught cider and bottled cider;

E330 citric acid – used as a synergist (to aid the effect of the anti-oxidant used);

Pectolase – an enzyme used to destroy residual pectin (a fruit starch) in keg and bottled cider and perry. This neutral substance (pectin) remains in real cider and perry which is not processed, and especially in rough cider ('scrumpy'), giving what is known in the West Country as 'a moonlight haze'.

In general, apples are blended from several orchards and varieties to produce a particular scrumpy style, and in one case apples and pears are combined to produce Pider – see Franklins, below.

Some of the best-known real ciders include Aspall's (organic) Cyder, Hartland's Medium, Heck's Sweet, Plum Tree Medium, Berrow Hill Dry, Dunkerton's Breakwell Seedling, Kinross Dry, Wilkins' Medium Sweet, Vickery's Dry, Baker's Dry and two perries (Hartland's Dry and Summers' Dry) and finally Franklins' Pider, a combination of cider and perry. There are other real ciders and real perries to be had, depending upon where you happen to be feeling a thirst. Licensees of real-ale pubs are often willing to point the enquiring (or confused!) drinker in the right direction, even to a rival pub.

Try it by all means, but it is as well to be careful when sampling scrumpy, as noted in an old rhyme from Oxfordshire which carries a detailed warning on the likely effects:

Drink rough cider as much as yer please,
Lose yer teeth and bow yer knees,
Sours yer gut and makes yer wheeze,
Turns yer words to stings o' bees,
Thins yer blood (but kills yer fleas),
Drink rough cider as much as yer please ...

# 4 Real cider-making

Real perries and "piders"
(made from a mixture of apples and pears)
are produced by similar methods.

```
           Washed
           apples
              │
              ▼
          Crusher/
          strainer
              │
              ▼
        Fermenting  ◄──────  Cultured yeast
           vat                 (optional)
              │
              ▼
          Racking
        (syphoning)
              │
              ▼
          Maturing
              │
              ▼
           Cask  ──────►  Bottling
```

4 The simple technique used to make "real" (unfiltered) cider, which is often
called "Scrumpy" or "rough cider". Where a cultured yeast is not employed, the
ferment begins spontaneously, but results are less predictable. This method is
universal among small producers.

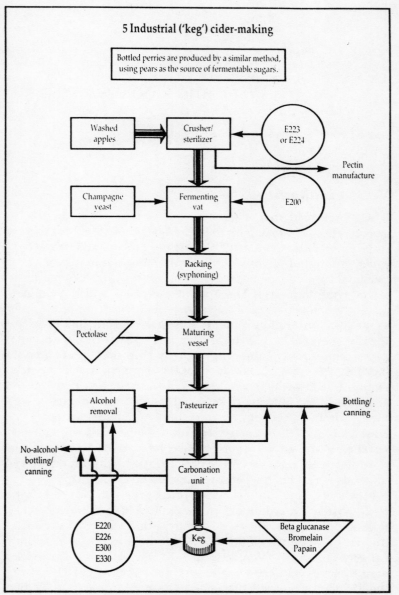

# 5 Industrial ('keg') cider-making

Bottled perries are produced by a similar method, using pears as the source of fermentable sugars.

Washed apples → Crusher/sterilizer ← E223 or E224

→ Pectin manufacture

Champagne yeast → Fermenting vat ← E200

Racking (syphoning)

Pectolase → Maturing vessel

Alcohol removal ← Pasteurizer → Bottling/canning

No-alcohol bottling/canning

Carbonation unit

E220 E226 E300 E330 → Keg ← Beta glucanase Bromelain Papain

5 The method used throughout Britain, Europe and the USA to produce bright ("keg") ciders and most bottled ciders. Ninety per cent of cider worldwide is produced by this method, which creates, as in keg ales and lagers, a long-lasting refined product. Pectolase is the sole enzyme used in cider-making, following the ferment, though some "giants" may use those shown within the larger triangle. Pectin is used as a thickener in many food products.

# 5   Wine and Coolers

And wine can of their wits the wise beguile.

Horace, Odyssey

## Vin Extraordinaire

It has been said that wine is as old as time. This may be an exaggeration, because both mead and beer are older, but wine is unquestionably a drink with historic influences and effects.

Depending upon how you define time, you may have a personal view of age and 'ageing' (another word for 'maturing' in the wine industry). The ancient Assyrians and Babylonians certainly enjoyed their wild yeast-fermented drink made from grape juice but, unlike modern winemakers, they had to accept the raw material in its natural form, each year's crop (and wine) depending upon weather and winemaking skill. There was no 'fiddling' of vintages, nor label frauds; there was no commercial blending of dissimilar wine types, and there was certainly no additives-aided industry to promote their winning wines or feed their customers with evasive 'technology-intense' excuses for crass commercialism and exploitation. These early winemakers left the natural growth process of seepage, through the roots of the vine, to build into the juice of the grape a complex mixture of minerals which fed the yeast which created the drink.

Much later the Romans, who brought the vine across Europe to a hostile environment in Britain (where it never really flourished, even for the monks of the Middle Ages), introduced the first 'modern' additive – sulphur dioxide, which they extracted directly from sulphur. It was used in a capacity identical to its modern function in wine, beer and cider – to keep the drink for longer than its natural lifespan, but Roman drinkers were perhaps fortunate that they drank in ignorance of sulphur dioxide's less than healthy effects upon some human beings. They knew only the natural pleasures and pains that drinking can bring.

Over the centuries, the temptation to take commercial advantage of a drink which continued to grow in popularity was too great to resist. Several books of the early eighteenth and the nineteenth centuries catalogued the growing scandals.

*A Directory in the Making and Managing of British Wines* by John Davies, published in 1808, gave directions for the adulteration of many wines, including methods of reactivating those which had turned sour! Wine was also cautiously watered or its acidity modified by the use of slaked lime, while herbs were added to poor wine, which was then sold as muscatel.

A few years later, in 1814, adulteration was accepted to such an extent that Phillip Carnell published, in a pamphlet on home winemaking, a recipe for making eighteen gallons of artificial claret, whose ingredients included:

2 pecks of claret vine leaves
40 lb raw sugar
½ lb powdered red tartar
6 handfuls rosemary leaves
6 oranges – peel and juice only
1 gallon or more of brandy
18½ gallons of soft water

This recipe was said to be very popular, and many people enjoyed the resulting 'wine', indicating just how easy it is to fake or adulterate such a drink in modern wineries, where there are many more aids to flavouring and modification than there were in 1814.

Modern winemakers are fond of describing their drinks as 'sophisticated products', suggesting that a great deal of expertise has gone into their creation. They should bear in mind that the term 'sophisticated' is often used in the wine retailing industry to indicate wines which have been adulterated!

Another relatively modern process is chaptalization, which involves adding cane sugar at the fermentation stage in order to increase the wine's alcoholic strength. This may be necessary during poor harvests of grapes, when their fructose content is low. Chaptalization was employed as long ago as 1801, when Jean Antoine Claude, Comte de Chanteloupe, published a tract on the subject. The process was not named, however, until Napoleon's time, when his Minister of Agriculture, Chaptal, gave it his formal blessing in the shape of a decree.

Unsophisticated wines (those which use no additives, and are therefore 'pure and simple') are just fermented fruit juice, the principal element of interest to the yeast being the simple sugar the juice contains – fructose.

In some wines in France, Germany and Italy, fermentation is aided by *Botrytis cinerea* (also known as 'noble rot') a wild fungus or 'bloom', which remains on the skins of the grapes and concentrates the sugars in the juice. The French Sauternes and the German Trockenbeeren wines are produced by this method.

Commercially, however, the whole of Europe ferments wine with cultured yeasts. That is not to say that these yeasts converse in the French or German equivalent of a BBC accent but that they are developed in the winemakers' laboratories, where they are specially selected and cross-bred with other strains to produce a range of flavours and effects in wine.

One such effect is achieved by a yeast with the ability to ferment particular components of the must, as the fermenting grape juice is called. In this way characteristics of acidity, fruit flavour and tannin 'bite' can be built into a wine. As the flow diagram on p.104 shows, modern winemaking is by no means the simple process of allowing yeast to feed on a sweet juice that thousands of winemakers exploited for centuries but now employs additives at virtually every stage of the activity. Fiddling is now the rule rather than the exception.

The list of substances and processes available to and permitted in use by the commercial winemaker is extensive. These details are listed in full in EEC Reg. 337 79: Oenological Practices Annex 111 (Official Journal of the European Communities).

At the fermentation stage, various yeast foods may be employed, including substances such as diammonium phosphate, ammonium sulphate or thiamine hydrochloride. If left for long enough, any fermented drink will clear naturally, but delay is commercially undesirable for the winemaker, who already suffers a marketing disadvantage due to the longer time wine needs to mature, this being due to its higher strength than beer or cider.

As a result, he often uses a variety of preparations, including albumen derived from eggs or dried blood powder, as well as refined clays such as 558 bentonite (also used to clarify lager), kaolin and kieselgühr to clear it faster. Later, after the fermentation, E200 sorbic acid, E202 potassium sorbate and another sulphur derivative, E224 potassium metabisulphite, may be added to the wine to kill off remaining yeast cells and organisms which have made their way into the must during the ferment, thus 'stabilizing it' in the parlance of the winemaker and brewer.

Such additives also appear as 'ingredients' of home winemaking kits available in the supplies shops. Potassium or sodium metabisulphite is available as Campden Tablets or in powder form. This is a highly reactive additive and can cause severe bronchial irritation if inhaled, which is always a possibility during mixing with water (especially hot water) for purposes of container-sterilizing.

Clearly, many commercially made wines also contain these substances, but there is no requirement for manufacturers to give any information about them to the person who is contemplating drinking such wines. Therefore asthmatics and persons who suffer with recurrent urticaria (nettle-rash) and who may be allergic to E220 sulphur dioxide or E210 benzoic acid, which are commonly used preservatives (the latter is also used in cola drinks), have no way of knowing what a drink may do to them. Any one of six variant forms of sulphur dioxide may appear in wines.

In 1985 the Dutch equivalent of the Consumers' Association (*Which?*) tested a batch of wines for home consumption and concluded that most contained higher than the EEC-recommended safe level of sulphur dioxide, showing that monitoring of foodstuff additives is slapdash at best, even in countries which exercise caution.

A similar test, of nineteen wines, by *Which?* itself in May 1986 revealed that several contained almost the maximum 'permitted' level of the preservative, meaning that someone who regularly drinks two glasses of red wine or 2½–3 glasses of white wine a day, could exceed the ADI (Acceptable Daily Intake) of the substance, with possibly serious implications for asthma- and urticaria-sufferers, as well as a higher risk of hangover generation.

Sulphur dioxide, in smaller quantities, is also used as a preservative and anti-microbial agent in beer and cider.

Excluding yeast foods and clarifying agents, some of which

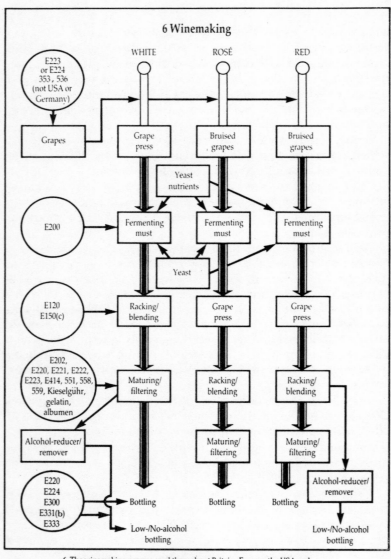

# 6 Winemaking

6 The winemaking process used throughout Britain, Europe, the USA and Australia. The press is used before fermentation for white wine and after it for rosé and red wine. Black (red) grapes are removed early from the ferment to achieve a pink colour in rosé wines. Additives are shown being introduced to white wine for simplicity – they are used identically at all stages of all forms. Some organic winemakers limit their additives use to small amounts of E220 sulphur dioxide, 558 bentonite and 559 kaolin at the maturing/filtering stage. Some wines are pasteurized after this stage – in particular, some full-bodied red wines and sweet table wines (red and white). In this event, some preservatives may be omitted.

are referred to above, the principal additives to wine are:

E120 cochineal – used as a colouring matter in red wines and soft drinks, in its form as ammonium carmine.

E150(c) ammonia caramel – used as a colouring matter.

E170 calcium carbonate (chalk) – used as a de-acidifier. Chalk is alkaline.

E200 sorbic acid – used as a pH factor adjuster and anti-fungal agent. The ideal pH for wine fermentation is 3.4 pH to 3.2 pH.

E202 potassium sorbate – used as a preservative in fermented wine.

E220 sulphur dioxide – used as a preservative in fermented wine.

E221 sodium sulphite – used as a preservative in fermented wine.

E222 sodium hydrogen sulphite – used as a preservative in fermented wine.

E223 sodium metabisulphite – used as a preservative in fermented wine.

E224 potassium metabisulphite – used as a preservative in fermented wine.

E300 L-ascorbic acid (vitamin C) – used as an anti-oxidant.

E331(b) diSodium citrate – used as a synergist (to aid the action of anti-oxidant E300, E332 or E336).

E332 triPotassium citrate – used as an anti-oxidant.

E333 triCalcium citrate – used as an acid flavour buffer in fermented wine.

E336 diPotassium L-tartrate – used as an anti-oxidant.

E414 gum arabic – used as a clarifying agent.

536 potassium ferrocyanide – used as a component of blue finings.

558 bentonite – used as a clarifying agent.

casein – used as a clarifying agent

kieselgühr – used as a clarifying agent.

## Blue Finings

Grape juice sometimes contains relatively high amounts of iron and/or copper, either because of the presence of these metals in the water table feeding the vine or because of pick-up from iron or copper containers. These metals in the must affect fermentation rate and efficiency as well as flavour, so they are often removed from white and rosé wine by a process called 'blue finings'. The principal constituent is potassium ferrocyanide, which is banned from use in Germany and the USA. See Appendix 2.

## Sustenance for the Snob

Much has been written and debated about wine snobs. The 'species' arose because various drinks are placed in a (fallacious) social pecking-order, with the same rules applying as to the affectations of other areas of human endeavour, such as painting and music. The wine snob tends to concentrate on trivia such as the 'significance' of particular labels and vintages, the majesty of noble wines and over-written histories of the vine and the winemaker.

The respective assumed social levels of alcoholic drinks place spirits, especially whisky (or whiskey) and brandy as the typical drinks of the military, political and social élite, beer and cider as the drinks of artisans and manual workers, and wine as the drink of the professional or middle classes.

At its worst but most significant social level, wine is directly responsible for a classic male-chauvinist epithet, 'wine, women and song' – in which women come second.

At its most insufferable, wine promotes literary excess, where natural enthusiasm (which the intelligent drinker balances against information and experience) goes crazy. Some of the potted biographies of the winemaker or the wine are sketched so colourfully as to be worthy of inclusion in *Private Eye*'s Pseud's Corner. Here is an example:

Our Cabernet Sauvignon is a dry, medium-bodied elegant red wine. It has a deep ruby colour and a delicate cedar aroma. This wine is rich with varietal flavours suggesting blackcurrants and a hint of chocolate, balanced by nuances of oak on the finish. Food accompanying an aged Cabernet should be simple but elegantly prepared to allow the mellowed tannins and full fruit flavour to develop. Cabernet Sauvignon, surprisingly, is also a good match with a chocolate-cherry cake. The combined complexity of fruit, acid and tannin in the wine are complemented by the tartness of the cherries and the rich, intense texture and taste of the chocolate.

I thought it was just a bottle of wine until I read the label, which occupied a 12½ cm (5 in) by 7.5 cm (3 in) area on the reverse of the bottle, an ideal spot for a list of ingredients!

The truth is that much wine lore is just legend, or the modern advertising copywriter's imaginative concoction. People know what they like, or like to talk about in terms of drinks, although for some reason wine snobs don't often chat about Marcobrunner Riesling Trockenbeerenauslese Cabinet – unless they want to run out of breath, that is. 'Claret' drops much more readily from the lips.

Wine-tasting and TV quizzes at Christmas serve only to confirm that all taste is subjective and that the best test of a wine is made with your own taste-buds. In the course of a court hearing in France a few years ago, a certain M. Lionel, a wine-shipper, explained: 'There are certain laboratories whose sole job it is to improve bad Bordeaux wines. It is very difficult to taste a young wine in particular and place it accurately.' At the same hearing, a Swiss dealer said that, 'Even chemical analysis cannot tell where a wine comes from.'

Diogenes refused to have any truck with the wine-tasting charade. When asked which wine he preferred, he replied: 'Somebody else's.'

## What, no 'Campaign for Real Wine'?

The movement which emerged from the Society for the preservation of Beer from the Wood, to become CAMRA (Campaign for Real Ale) in 1971, gained force because of its conviction that natural beer, as opposed to processed beer, was about to disappear from Britain. The large brewers had taken advantage of their technical ability to overcome the air-tainting problems from which beers of all types, in their most popular form – draught, suffer. They adopted the keg process, which blankets the beer with carbon dioxide, preventing immediate oxidation, after pasteurizing it.

Although wine is similarly subject to the effects of air (hence its maturation in large casks and in bottles), it is not generally available in a draught form, so the immediate problem of oxidation did not present itself, unlike real ale, which needs the oxidizing effect of the air if its full flavour is to be brought out. However, this need for air contact limits its life, a reasonable trade-off if you like good beer.

Further, the great majority of wines available in Britain are imported, making a British Campaign for Real Wine toothless from the start. With the large brewery combines resident in Britain and producing the home-drunk product, CAMRA could exert some influence on beer matters and may also have been influential in the development of microbreweries (boutique breweries) in the USA and Canada.

Wine has become the world's most fashionable drink, and such is the enthusiasm among its drinkers that they would probably consider Austrian wine, vintage 1984, to be superior to the apparently more pure long drinks.

Campaigns are definitely not for wine-drinkers!

## Trying to Define 'Organic Wine'

Having considered the criteria by which pure beers and ciders may be judged, can we apply the same criteria to wine? Since very few commercial winemakers are producing truly additive-free wines, the comparisons cannot be exact, but there are ways of searching out safer alternatives to mass-produced, additive-laden examples of the drink.

Perhaps organic wine, which depends upon the adherence of the winemaker to certain agreed standards, makes the closest approach to what we might term 'real wine'; this is known as 'biological wine' in Germany, although since many winemakers in both Germany and France use the chaptalization process (adding cane sugar to the ferment in order to increase alcoholic strength), such definitions are open to question. Perhaps a near-pure version is mead, an English country wine fermented from honey, although this is technically a liqueur.

Some German and French wines are also given artificial body by the addition of cane sugar syrup or grape juice *after* the ferment, lending additional sweetness and depth. Since cane sugar is a refined product, these wines cannot be considered 'green' or 'organic' in the accepted sense of the two terms.

Organic food is, loosely, any food produced without the use of artificial (synthetic) fertilizers or pesticides. It remains a problem, even after several years of the use of the term and many centuries of so-called 'organic farming', to decide which dry foods are truly additive-free on this basis, and even more difficult to decide which wines are additive-free, although beer categorization is not so difficult.

Some British, French, German, Italian, Spanish and American winemakers produce organic wine. In general, they follow a certification process which promotes the 'natural' image of their products, without the wines themselves necessarily being additive-free.

Many such wines are therefore A HEALTHIER ALTERNATIVE TO MASS-PRODUCED WINES (even those with centuries of history), containing lower amounts of sulphur dioxide or its variants than are permitted by EEC regulations. Many such winemakers provide information upon request concerning vinification methods, such as chaptalization, sulphur treatment, filtering and fining.

Each winemaker is required by the organizing body to sign agreements, keep documentary records and adhere to guidelines on materials and methods.

## Identifying Organic Wines by Symbols or Labels

European and American organic wines may have the following classification names or symbols shown on labels:

| | |
|---|---|
| *France*: | Nature et Progrès (symbol may show 'Terre et Ocean') |
| | Terre et Vie (Land and Life) |
| *Germany*: | Biokreis |
| | Bioland |
| | Bundesverband Okologischer Weinbau (BOW) – the controlling organization |
| | Demeter (also a British organic standard) |
| | Naturland |
| | Oinos |
| *Italy*: | Suole e Salute |
| *Spain*: | Vida Sana |
| *USA*: | CCOF (California Certified Organic Farmers) |

Some Australian growers and winemakers produce organic wines, but do not adhere to any European or American organic standards as such. This may be because many list all additives used and all must list preservatives. As with American wines these labels are often obscured by another label when they appear abroad.

Many French organic wines carry a description on the label, indicating growth-media free from synthetic fertilizers but never indicating a fermentation process which excludes additives. These descriptions may replace or augment the symbols or names shown above and include the following descriptive phrases: *'sans produits chimique'*, *'sans engrais chimique'*, *'systeme biologique'* *'ni herbicide'*, *'ni insecticide de synthèse'* and occasionally 'made from unsprayed grapes'. The principal insecticide and anti-fungal agent sprayed on grapes is copper sulphate. Only minute amounts are found in wine.

In some winemaking countries, especially France and Spain, makers may refrain from making claims about their organic wines, some because they are unaware that such claims could help to sell them, others because of a general agreement in the trade that such publicity confers an unfair advantage on the organic winemaker.

Further, there are many small family or village winemaking concerns in Spain, in particular, where the wine is 'organic' because the winemakers have not yet heard about additives!

## Selected Organic Wines

The following named wines are available from specialist wine suppliers in Britain and the USA and from off-licences and supermarkets in Britain, France, Spain and Germany:

*England* (English table wines)
Avalon Vineyard English Table Wine, 1985
Lurgashall Winery Country Wines (elderflower, gooseberry and English Table Wine)
Sedlescombe Vineyard Gewürtztraminer
Sedlescombe Gutenborer
Sedlescombe Muller Thurgau
Sedlescombe Reichsteiner
*France*
Carte d'Or Champagne José Ardinat
Saumur Méthode Champenoise Brut Gérard Leroux

RED WINES
*France (Provence, South)*
Domaine Anthea 1987 Cépage Merlot (available at Safeway foodstores)

Domaine de Clairac Jougla Vin de Table
Domaine de l'Ile Vin de Pays de l'Aude
*France (Bordeaux)*
Château Tour de Beaupoil, 1988
Château des Meaumes, 1986 (available at Majestic Wine Warehouses)
Château du Moulin de Peyronin AC, 1986
Château Renaissance AC, 1986
Château de Prade Bordeaux Supérieur AC, 1985
Château Méric Graves AC, 1985
Château Barrail des Graves St-Emilion AC, 1986
Domaine St-Anne-entre-deux-mers AC, 1986 (available at Safeway Food Stores)
*France (Rhone)*
Côte du Rhone crû du Coudoulet
Cave le Vigneronne Villedieu AC, 1986 (14 per cent ABV)
Vignoble de la Jasse AC, 1985
Domaine St-Apollinaire AC Côtes du Rhône 1985 and 1986 (available at Sainsbury stores)
*France (Burgundy)*
Macon Alain Guillot AC, 1986
Bourgogne Alain Guillot AC, 1986
*France (Beaujolais)*
Château de Boisfranc Beaujolais Supérieur AC, 1987
*Italy*
Chianti DOCG Roberto Drighi, 1986
Valpolicella DOC Classico Superiore, 1985
*Spain*
Valdepenas, 1985 – Vino Tinto Cosecha
Biovin Valdepenas DOC, 1986
*USA*
Four Chimneys Kingdom Red
Four Chimneys Primeur Red
Frey Natural Wines Cabernet Sauvignon, 1984

WHITE WINES
*France (Loire)*
Blanc de Blancs Guy Bossard
Muscadet de Sèvre et Maine sur Lie Guy Bossard AC, 1986
*France (Bordeaux)*
Château Ballue Mondon Sec AC, 1986

*Name Your Poison!*

Château le Barradis Monbazillac AC, 1985
*France (Burgundy)*
Bourgogne Rouge Alain Guillot AC, 1986 (not a red, a rouge, i.e.
bronze-coloured – Chardonnay grape)
*France (Alsace)*
Sylvaner Pierre Frick AC, 1986
Gewürztraminer Pierre Frick AC, 1986
*Germany (Baden)*
Bahlinger Silberberg, 1986
Weissburgunder, 1986
Muller Thurgau Kabinett Trocken, 1985
*Germany (Mosel-Saar-Ruwer)*
Briedeler Nonnengarten, 1986
Riesling Kabinett, 1986
*Germany (Rheinhessen)*
Riesling Halbtrocken, 1986
Rulander Spätlese, 1984
Silvaner Trocken, 1986
Muller Thurgau Kabinett Trocken, 1985
Silvaner, 1982
*Germany (Rheinpfalz)*
Rulander Kabinett, 1986
*Italy*
San Vito Verdiglio Roberto Drighi, 1986
Soave DOC Classico, 1986: Guerrieri – Rizzardi

## The English Difference

There are 200 operating wineries, with vineyards attached, in
England. Those in Scotland and Wales, some of which produce
wine from grape concentrates, would fall within the EEC
classification 'British Winemakers'. According to EEC wine law,
all wines produced from English-grown grapes must be termed
'English Table Wine'. No change in this specification is
envisaged following the removal of trade-barriers in 1992.

The principal grape grown in England is Muller Thurgau,
although wines (mainly white wines) are also produced from
Riesling, Sylvaner, Chardonnay and hybrid forms such as
Seyval.

Three main organizations lay down standards for English
organic winemakers: Demeter, the OFG1 (Organic Farmers and

Growers) and the Soil Association. Relevant names or symbols appear on wine-bottle labels. As with European organic wines, producers who adhere to these standards follow assumptions concerning culture media (soil treatments) and not necessarily additive-free fermenting/maturing methods.

## Coolers

The most modern alcoholic drink is called a 'cooler' – or, in the USA, which is where it originated, a 'wine cooler' or 'spritzers', which could cause some confusion with glass receptacles for the cooling of white wine.

Coolers are essentially wine, mainly white wine or cider, combined with fruit juices or fruit flavourings and carbonated (fizzy) water. They are aimed at the summer drinks market, and their strength at the lower end is pitched at a point (rather suspiciously) where they just miss the need to label ingredients. However, two such coolers are at or below the labelling cut-off point and therefore indicate the above-mentioned ingredients as well as sugar, E330 citric acid and E211 sodium benzoate, a preservative.

Changes in revenue favour these drinks, and producers can hardly be blamed for taking advantage of a Chancellor of the Exchequer's Budget Day endorsement of their 'health benefits' (March 1988) and the avoidance of the need to list ingredients.

In the list which follows, Babycham (a perry) and Snowball (an advocaat) are included because of their alcoholic similarity to coolers.

| COOLER BRAND NAME | Alcohol-content (% by volume) |
| --- | --- |
| Apple Splitz* | 1.2 |
| Arena | 4.8 |
| Babycham | 3.5 |
| Diamond Blush Cider Cooler (Taunton Cider Co.) | 5.0 |
| Lotus Light (orange) | 4.5 |
| Lotus Light (tropical fruit) | 4.5 |
| Palm Beach Melon | 4.0 |
| Palm Beach Mure (blackberry) | 4.0 |

| | |
|---|---|
| Passion Splitz* | 1.2 |
| Paul Masson Spectrum (lemon) | 4.5 |
| Paul Masson Spectrum (mango) | 4.5 |
| Paul Masson Spectrum (orange) | 4.5 |
| Sainsbury's Spritzer (orange) | 5.0 |
| Sainsbury's Spritzer (original) | 5.0 |
| Sainsbury's Spritzer (summer fruit) | 6.5 |
| Snowball | 3.0 |
| St Leger | 3.5 |
| St Michael Orange Fizz | 5.5 |
| St Michael Spritzer | 5.5 |
| St Michael Tropical | 5.0 |
| Taunton Cool | 3.0 |
| West Coast Cooler | 3.5 |

* Labelled to show ingredients

# 6 Spirits

Claret is the liquor for boys, port for men, but he who aspires to be a
hero must drink brandy.

Samuel Johnson

## Strong and Noble Types

Whether or not Dr Johnson appreciated the punning connection
is not recorded, but the most alcoholically potent drinks have
probably achieved modern commercial importance because of
the inventive mind of one man, whose name almost describes
the usual (and ineffective) antidote to a hangover: Aeneas
Coffey, an Irish excise officer, who in 1831 invented the patent
still, which is also known as the Coffey Still.

Spirit drinks are produced by the process of distillation, which
exploits the chemistry of liquids in that different liquid
substances boil at different temperatures. By heating such
substances in enclosed conditions it is possible to separate the
main elements of, for example, crude mineral oil to yield
bitumen (a tar-like material used to surface roads), the two
'motor spirits', paraffin and petrol (or, as the Americans
correctly describe it, gasoline), methanol and ethylene glycol,
which is used universally as an antifreeze medium in motor
vehicles.* This process is called 'catalytic cracking', and another
of its mineral oil by-products is diethylene glycol, which has an
undesirable relationship with Austrian wine in particular!
Further oil 'cracking' processes create detergents and plastics
such as polythene, but the more palatable results of distillation
include malt whisky, grain whisky, brandy, gin, rum and vodka,
the so-called 'noble spirits'.

As its name implies, malt whisky, which is probably the
world's favourite spirit drink, is derived from an alcoholic
infusion of malt. Before distillation is embarked upon, the
processing of ingredients is almost identical to that of beer.

* So-called 'coal-tar' dyes are also petroleum products.

Liquid malt is fermented by yeast and later heated, the evaporated alcohol being condensed, matured and bottled.

Brandy is distilled wine; gin is a distilled grain infusion (sometimes malt) which is flavoured with juniper, coriander and orris; rum is distilled from fermented molasses or refined cane sugar, and vodka is a purified spirit derived from rye, while bourbon is a type of whiskey distilled from an infusion of maize. In the case of vodka, much of the hangover potential is removed by purification, but so is much of the flavour to be found in, for example, Irish Whiskey. In general, all forms of whisky apart from that produced in Scotland (i.e. 'Scotch') are distinguished by the addition of the letter 'e' before the 'y'.

Distillation of edible spirits for drinking is by no means a modern phenomenon: the Chinese are known to have distilled from rice wine (saké) in ancient times. Throughout history, alcoholic distillation has been an essential element in the general diet and ritual feasting of many societies. Captain Cook discovered that the inhabitants of the Pacific Islands knew how to extract spirit from alcoholic infusions of fruit and tree-bark juices.

Commercially, in modern times, spirits intended for human consumption (many other forms are distilled for industrial purposes) are strictly controlled in terms of revenue details, but not in terms of their ingredients, which may be derived from numerous alcoholic distillate sources. These edible spirits are manufactured to different strengths, and although the Food Labelling Regulations require that they be described as 'under strength' when below forty per cent alcohol by volume and must show a strength figure above this point, the 'proof spirit' method of classification is still in use, although it is gradually being replaced by percentage alcohol by volume.

## Getting Up Steam

The way in which spirits are produced is probably the most efficient process in drinks-production, and in its most modern form the technique brings huge savings (and profits) to the distiller.

Of the two main forms of still in universal operation, the pot still, or alembic, essentially a crude alcohol-extractor, maintains its validity for three main reasons:

(1) its use produces a drink with greater flavour than those emerging from the patent still;

(2) it aids the 'simply produced and matured' image of many malt whiskies;

(3) it is simple to use and is ideal as an apparatus for distilling spirit drinks illegally – one simply heats an alcoholic infusion and condenses the spirit.

Although following the relaxation of licensing controls in the Budget of 1963 it became legal to brew beer or make wine at home without a licence, in Britain it remains illegal for unlicensed persons to distil spirits; a licence for the latter will not readily be made available! In some countries, home brewing remains illegal, notably in the Soviet Union.

Nevertheless, it is a vicariously gratifying detail for many citizens that, when a tax is introduced, some persons will make strenuous and subtle efforts to evade it. The acute shortage of revenue appreciation societies suggests that the inherent greed of governments for unearned income from an ever-growing range of chemically dubious substances has not gone unnoticed.

Enter the poteen (or potheen) distiller, with all his (or her) image of free Irish romanticism. What a shame that most of the image really is romantic fiction. Aside from the fact that pot stills charged up with infusions of potato and carrot and operated in the home can produce high amounts of methanol (wood spirit) in the drink (hence the stories about poteen making people 'blind drunk'), those who have tasted the stuff generally go back to branded varieties. I am told that the flavour-range varies from 'essence of cauliflower' to Patrick's Special Old Metal Polish in most poteen examples.

The branded (legitimate) varieties of spirit drink, whose labels contain no ingredient details, except for ABV, are produced by means of both the pot still and the patent still.

In its most basic (and sometimes illegal) form, the pot still is a single retort, of the type shown on p.125. Such stills can produce spirits with very dangerous constituents. The modern whisky pot still consists of two main units – a wash still and a spirit still, this set-up eliminating much of the undesirable matter, such as crude alcohols (fusel oil etc), unfermentable solids and yeast from the initial ferment.

Part of the output of the spirit still – foreshots and feints – may be fed later to the patent still for a third stage of distillation. Most grain whiskeys and nearly all brandies are produced by double or triple distillation. In the production of Cognac brandy (the *'appellation controllé'* of the type), the first distillate is called *brouilli* and contains about twenty-eight per-cent ABV. The second distillate, called *bonne chauffé*, contains about seventy-two per cent ABV. After distillation and maturation, all spirit drinks are watered to the correct alcohol concentration (usually forty per cent ABV) before bottling, unless they are 'under strength', i.e. less than forty per cent. Strangely, publicity material from the distilleries does not mention the watering-down process!

Don't be fooled by the stars on a bottle of brandy – they indicate nothing, nor does the term 'brandy' always indicate that grapes have been used to produce the drink, which derives its name from the Dutch term *brandewijn*, meaning a drink made by burning wine. False brandies include Calvados (mainly from France), which is distilled from apple liquor or cider and is known in the USA as 'applejack', kirsch, which is distilled from cherry liquor, and slivovitz, a Yugoslavian spirit prepared from plums. This may be called quetsch in some areas.

Whisky-drinkers who obtained promotional bottles of a certain Japanese spirit drink were no doubt utterly bemused by an explanation which accompanied the offer: 'This fine old whisky has been made only from the finest Scottish grapes.' Since this was not a Scottish malt whisky, it should have been spelt 'whiskey', but that's the least of the drinker's problems. Whisky-type spirits appear in so many different forms and from so many different distilling media that a review of false or fake versions would be a mammoth undertaking.

Aguardiente is a spirit distilled from either grapes or molasses, and this term, the Spanish word for spirit, may sometimes be applied to tequila, the Mexican spirit distilled from pulque, the fermented sap of the maguey plant, a cactus-like vegetable. This spirit drink is related to mescal, the Mexican spirit/hallucinogen which novelist Aldous Huxley tried on himself experimentally.

One point concerning Irish whiskey is worthy of special note: it is produced from a mash of grains (mainly barley), only half of which is malted, plus some wheat and oats. The use of oats is peculiar to Irish distilling, as it is to Irish brewing – it is also used in stout.

Where the colourless (white) spirits are concerned, many vodkas are distilled from other grains apart from rye, and sometimes from white cane sugar, which also forms the fermenting base for a neutral spirit called aquavit, a favourite drink in Scandinavian countries, where it is often flavoured with caraway. This drink, like many other spirit drinks, is known in Germany as Schnapps.

## Minor Additions

Of all alcoholic drinks, spirits probably contain the least number of additives. This is due to neither gastronomic nor health considerations on the part of the distillers but because the high alcohol-content of the drinks makes preservatives unnecessary. This does not mean, however, that they are necessarily any more healthy – the principal undesirable effects of spirits upon drinkers, such as an increased likelihood of gullet cancers and stomach ulcers, as well as more rapid liver damage, means that they are probably the most dangerous of drinks.

Only two additives are 'permitted' in spirit drinks, both as colourants:

In whisky and brandy   E150(b) caustic sulphite caramel
In liqueurs                 E160(b) annatto (also known as bixin or norbixin)

If a drinker is intent upon drinking the purest spirit available, the most sensible approach is to look for the lightest in colour. Most white spirits are free from colouring but may be treated with flavourings, some of them natural but others synthetic. Distillers maintain that their finest products, such as single malt whiskies, derive colouring only from the oak casks in which they are aged. I am sceptical of this claim.

## Liqueurs – Singing the Blues?

Liqueurs are very popular, and in view of the fact that only one colouring matter is officially 'permitted', the spirit-drinker who is equipped with two eyes as well as a tongue and a cheque-book may, for example, wonder how blue liqueurs get their deep colour.

It could be a natural colour such as that which is derived from the fermented leaves of Isatis tinctoria, which was well known to Queen Boadicea and her valiant troops, because it is woad, or it could be one of the 'coal-tar' or azo dyes, which may not be drinker-friendly. Possibilities include additive 133 brilliant blue FCF, a synthetic 'coal-tar' dye which is banned in Austria, Belgium, Denmark, Greece, Italy, Spain, Switzerland, Norway, Sweden and Germany, but more likely E132 indigo carmine, another 'coal-tar' dye.

Liqueurs are essentially sweet in flavour – the term 'liqueur' is derived from the French *liqueur de dessert*, meaning a sweet drink taken with the dessert, and many forms exist, including the following, which may or may not be artificially coloured:

Apry – an apricot 'brandy'

Benedictine – based upon a Cognac. The initials DOM which appear on the label do not signify Dirty Old Man but *Deo Optimo Maximo* ('To God, most good, most great').

Chartreuse – the green version is stronger than the yellow!

Cherry brandy – a cherry-flavoured brandy, but not distilled from cherries

Cointreau – brandy, flavoured with oranges

Crème de Cacao – brandy or neutral spirit flavoured with cocoa

Crème de Menthe – mint-flavoured brandy

Curaçao – white rum; available in orange or blue forms

Drambuie – whisky-based with heather honey flavourings

Galliano – an Italian liqueur based upon neutral spirit and flavoured with herbs. It is yellow in colour.

Grand Marnier – flavoured with oranges

Irish Mist – an Irish whiskey liqueur

Kahlua – a Mexican liqueur flavoured with coffee

Kümmel – neutral spirit flavoured with aniseed, caraway or cumin

Malibu – white rum flavoured with coconut

Maraschino – a cherry-flavoured brandy

Ouzo – neutral spirit flavoured with aniseed or mastic, which resembles licorice.

Pernod – flavoured with aniseed. This liqueur-type drink replaced absinthe, which was flavoured with wormwood, a poisonous herb.

Prunella – flavoured with plums

Retsina – a Greek vermouth flavoured with pine resin

Southern Comfort – peach-flavoured grain whiskey (USA)

Strega – citrus-flavoured neutral spirit (Italy)

Tia Maria – coffee-flavoured rum (Jamaica)

All such liqueurs are sweetened with cane sugar in varying degrees, making them, in combination with their high alcohol-content (23–35 per cent by volume), the most fattening of alcoholic drinks, volume for volume.

Where the colouring of most liqueurs is concerned, little information is available and is likely to remain so. Although the food advisory committees are not known for their forthright condemnation of dubious commercial practices in the food industry, nor for warnings about possible dangers in foods, the members of the Food Standards Committee were moved to make the following statement on colours in 1954: 'We cannot accept the contention that because 'coal-tar' colours have been used in food for many years without giving rise to complaints of illness, they are, therefore, harmless substances. Such negative evidence, in our view, merely illustrates that in the amounts customarily used in food the colours are not acutely toxic but gives no certain indication of any possible chronic effects. Any chronic effects would be insidious and it would be difficult, if not impossible, to attribute them with certainty to the consumption of food containing colouring matter.'

The FSC also said at the time: 'The possible carcinogenic properties of coal-tar dyes in food cannot be ignored', and in a further comment: 'In the absence of conclusive evidence we are unable to recommend any colour unreservedly as safe.'

YOU HAVE BEEN WARNED!

## The Pseudo-spirits

Ask most Martini Bianco or Cinzano Bianco drinkers which category their favourite drink falls within and they are likely to say 'light spirits'.

This is incorrect, because these drinks are slightly fortified wines, of the vermouth type, in which herbs have been marinated. Their strength falls within the range 13–17 per cent by volume. Most are fortified with gin, vodka, or neutral spirit.

As with most such wines, there is no requirement to list ingredients; some of these 'socially acceptable spirits' may contain residues from up to twenty-five different herbs. Aperitif wines such as Dubonnet Red and Campari (a 'bitter' aperitif) are similar concoctions, and port, sherry and Madeira also fall within this category, although it is thought that these drinks, which are wines fortified with brandy, are additive-free (Campari's strength may reach 24 per cent ABV).

Until the nineteenth century, however, it was commonplace for producers of port wine (which by definition and legal statute may come only from Oporto, Portugal) to add elderberry juice as a colourant.

## Speed Check

Candy is dandy, but liquor is quicker.

Ogden Nash

Mr Nash had that right, but there's more to it than he thought. Although spirits are the most concentrated form of alcoholic drink, the technique of 'chasing' a spirit drink with a long drink, such as lager or cider, speeds up the effect of the alcohol and generates a more powerful hangover than the spirit drink alone.

This is due partly to the mixed drink's having greater volume and a higher alcohol-content than the long drink alone. This increased volume covers a greater area of gullet and stomach lining, causing faster assimilation.

The alcohol-content of many 'chased' drinks also adds up to a significant level in terms of the action of a group of muscles at the outlet of the stomach. See 'Drinkers' Delusions' (chapter 10).

## Perestroika Moonshine

Following the official clampdown on alcohol in the Soviet Union in 1985, a part of Mikhail Gorbachev's programme of *perestroika* (restructuring), the rocketing price of alcoholic drinks has reactivated widescale home brewing and home distilling, both of which activities are illegal in the Soviet Union. Samogon, the home-produced moonshine distilled from cane sugar, is said to possess characteristics no more subtle than those of its Irish opposite number.

The effects of price-controlled prohibition can be seen in the number of illegal distillers who appear before the Soviet courts: in 1985, approximately 80,000 were convicted, the number rising to 397,000 by 1987; in the first two months of 1988, an initial count of 130,000 convictions suggested an extrapolated final total of one million. No fewer than 11,000 Soviet citizens are said to have died in 1987 after drinking samogon.

The Soviet authorities should consider the lesson of history. When the Temperance Movement energized the American government into bringing in Prohibition in 1920, they had no idea they might be setting up a new industry in illicit liquor and beer, with its own network of secret drinking-houses called 'speakeasies'.

With the repeal of the Prohibition legislation in 1933, the Prohibitionists, who had coined the term 'wet' for the liberals (drinkers) who declined to back their stringent measures against the demon drink, had to admit that the experiment had backfired, just as it appears to have done in the Soviet Union.

It might be argued that prohibition of alcohol was partly responsible when, early in March 1989, more than a hundred people in the Indian state of Gujarat died after drinking illicit home-made spirit. Gujarat is India's only 'dry' state.

# 7 Distilling

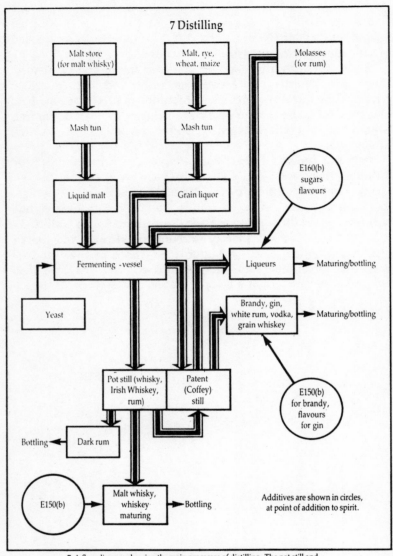

7 A flow diagram showing the main processes of distilling. The pot still and patent still are shown linked in respect of white spirits and grain whiskies – the output of the one feeds the other (feints). See patent still principle, following. High-quality whiskies such as the single malts (Glenfiddich etc) are often distilled by means of the pot still alone, but processes may be modified to produce a variety of heavy-bodied or light spirits. All are colourless (except pot-still whisky) when received from the still. The three primary malting stages for whisky (whiskey) are identical to those used in the brewing of beer (lager, ale and stout), except that peat is often used as the heating|source for the malt used in malt whisky, but only at the kilning/malting stages.

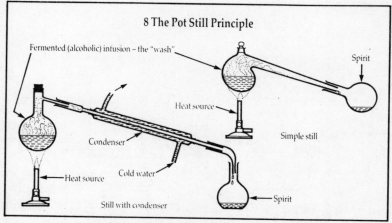

## 8 The Pot Still Principle

Fermented (alcoholic) infusion – the "wash"

Spirit

Heat source

Simple still

Condenser

Cold water

Heat source

Spirit

Still with condenser

8 The wash is heated directly, and condensation (distillation) is enhanced by the addition of a condenser. The aroma generated by distilling is exquisitely aromatic and is one reason why poteen and other bootleg liquor-distillers carry small portable pot stills on their travels. These "little pots" can be quickly transferred to a boat, and with luck a seaborne breeze will carry the revealing aroma away from the Revenue men's nostrils.

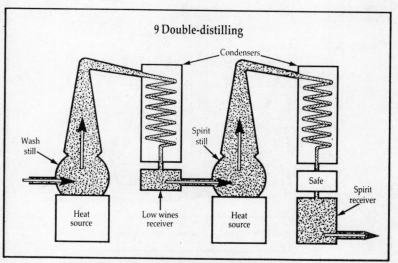

## 9 Double-distilling

Condensers

Wash still

Spirit still

Safe

Spirit receiver

Heat source

Low wines receiver

Heat source

9 Many malt whiskies are double-distilled by the technique shown above. The first distillate, called "low wines", is passed to the spirit still, and the liquor remaining in the wash still is discarded. Three main elements of spirit are received from the spirit still:

1) foreshots, the first products of distillation;
2) the "potable" (edible) spirit;
3) feints, the final products of distillation.

Foreshots and feints may be combined with fresh wash and fed to the patent still for a third stage of distillation. See Patent Still diagram, following.

# 10 The Coffey or Patent Still Principle

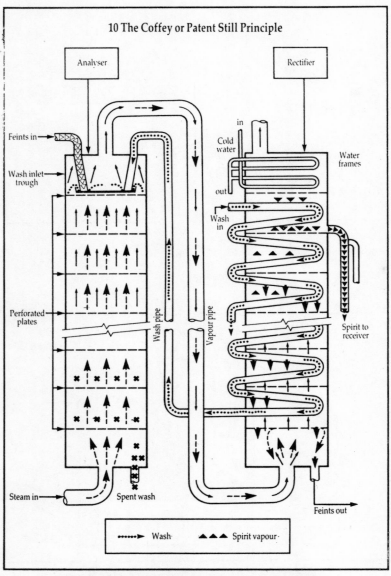

10 The fermented infusion of malt or grains (liquor or "wash") is introduced at the top of the rectifier and passed to the analyser, where it trickles through perforated copper plates. Rising steam evaporates the volatile elements of spirit and other solid materials and passes them to the rectifier, where they are condensed by a cold water frame and passed out to the receiver. The wash is the primary material of the patent still in this example, with feints being introduced from the output of the pot still (see Pot Still Principle, preceding). The patent still, unlike the pot still, can be operated continuously.

# 7 Cocktails

## Down Mexico Way

What is a cocktail? It's a liquid version of that well-known piece of string, because, to measure its effects, you might just as well double the distance from the middle to the end.

That is the cocktail's most insidious characteristic – you have no accurate method for deciding its alcoholic strength, unless you prepare it yourself from measured quantities.

The typical cocktail is usually a mixture of spirit, bitter aperitif or sweet vermouth, fruit juice and ice, plus a cherry or an olive, plus a twist of real lemon. It is usually very strong, in the order of 30 to 40 per cent ABV, understandable when you consider, say, the component essences of the Water Lily, this 'fluid flower' being typical of the often vaguely descriptive but always lurid names employed. This version contains gin, apricot brandy, bitter aperitif (such as Campari), orange juice and lemonade.

As a social phenomenon the cocktail is outrageously suave. Its appeal is the result of a colourful mix of potent and semi-mystical ingredients, including the supposedly higher thirst-quenching factor of ice, rather than mere water, the 'natural' garnish of a colourful fruit, and not least, its origin, which is still shrouded in the inebriated mists of time.

The drink as a distinct form probably had its beginnings in Mexico, or one of the Central American republics, during the nineteenth century. Modern explanations of its origin concentrate on rationalized derivations of the name, such as 'the tail that cocks up' or 'the tail of a cock' but the most literary origins are attributed to the name of an Aztec princess, Xochitl, who, it is said, presented a drink to a king with startling romantic results.

A mixed drink from the French region known in ancient times

as Gironde (Bordeaux) called Coquetel is also credited as the first cocktail, but no matter how they first came about, the term 'health drink' does not exactly spring to mind to further describe these potent concoctions in small glasses. Delicious though they are, cocktails are potentially very risky drinks. They may contain, in addition to a great deal of alcohol, herb residues from the vermouth, colour (possibly synthetic) from liqueurs, preservatives from fruit squash, sweeteners from low-calorie mixers, and further preservatives from the cherry or olive.

A drinker could only guess at the synergistic possibilities of a Manhattan Dry, for instance, which typically consists of Canadian whiskey, French vermouth, Angostura Bitters and a cherry.

## Shaken, not stirred

Ian Fleming's fictional character James Bond insisted that a dry Martini, which is mainly gin, should be shaken, and never stirred. Identical physical processes take place during both actions, but some cocktail drinkers (and enthusiasts behind the bar) say that to stir the mixture 'bruises' the gin. If you believe that, you will probably also believe that cocktails are organic works of nature.

The essential details of the generic forms of the drinks which make up a cocktail are spread throughout this book, so it would be superfluous to detail the complete range, most of which are variable creations at the bar, but some drinks which are thought to be cocktails (yet are normally only cocktail components) stand out from the crowd in terms of image. One of these is Pimm's, an English vermouth-type drink, intended for dilution. It is said to consist mainly of gin and red vermouth in its most popular form, Pimm's No.1 Cup.

James Pimm perfected his secret recipe in London in 1840, and named his creation Pimm's Gin Sling, which was clearly due for a revamp in modern times if it was going to be successful in an image-driven market! It has now been joined by Pimm's Vodka Cup, both drinks having a strength of 25 per cent ABV.

Enjoy your cocktail, but remember its abrasive elements: spirit, topped up with (alcoholic) vermouth, plus a rum-based bitter, plus a few colours, plus the urethane in a good slosh of fruit brandy, plus sulphur dioxide in the cherry, and you could name your own: Witches' Brew.

For me, one cocktail stands apart from Harvey Wallbanger (vodka-based), Corpse Reviver (brandy-based) or Rob Roy (whisky-based). To approach your very own Zero Hour add equal amounts of Pernod, Crème de Menthe, brandy, apricot brandy and ............ an olive.

## Mixers

The most vaguely defined drinks are those which fall within the general marketing classification of 'mixers', meaning a range of still or fizzy water-based preparations. They are used to extend a spirit or cocktail, or can be drunk alone. Those which are most often included under this loose term in supermarkets and off-licences are tonic waters, ginger ales, soda waters and fizzy fruit squashes or juices. The effect of their use upon the drinker is that of faster inebriation than by drinking the spirit or cocktail alone, since they are carbonated, they soften the sharp edge of the alcohol, extend the area of stomach covered, and avoid the slow-down effect of the pyloric sphincter (See Drinkers' Delusions, p.146). Details of additives and other constituents of mixers are covered generically in 'Soft Drinks' (chapter 8).

# 8   Soft Drinks

A soft drink turneth away company.

Oliver Herford

## Sweet and Bubbly

You don't need high technology skills to produce a soft drink – it's just a mixture of fruit juices, flavourings, sweeteners and acids, but there is plenty of after-the-event skill employed to promote the drink and keep it in good condition on the supermarket shelf.

Since all such drinks must be labelled to show their ingredients, in theory their main constituents are known to the drinker, but misleading labelling is becoming so common and the consequences so confusing, that it is worth reviewing the vital details.

The first thing that strikes a perceptive soft-drinks shopper, browsing in the supermarket or the off-licence, is that the food industry generally has moved to take advantage of the emotive term 'free', including it on labels which proclaim 'free from artificial preservatives' or 'free from artificial colours'.

An example of this new-found freedom in promotional or descriptive material is that on labels on cans of a well-known 'slimming' cola drink: 'CAFFEINE-FREE, SUGAR-FREE. Ingredients: carbonated water, colour (caramel), artificial sweetener (aspartame), phosphoric acid, flavourings, citric acid, preservative (E211), contains phenylalinine.' Information about the nature and biological effects of these ingredients is covered in Appendix 2. I think that I would prefer to take my chances with caffeine and sugar. The prospective imbiber of soft drinks would have to guess what the 'flavourings' may be (the maker may include dozens of flavours under this description), were this label the only source of information.

# Coke is it, but what is it?

In cola drinks, flavourings are drawn from the cola nut, which is the fruit of the Cola acuminata, a tropical tree. Extract of cola nut includes caffeine (also found in tea and coffee). This vegetable alkaloid is habit-forming. Some people may be allergic to such substances, or dietetically intolerant. The distinction is that an allergy may be due to a missing enzyme (inability to digest milk due to a deficiency of lactase, for instance), while intolerance may result from over-use of a foodstuff.

However, vegetable alkaloids, which number includes theobromine (a constituent of cocoa) and cocaine, have potent and sometimes dangerous effects upon animal systems (i.e. human consumers). One of the most obvious examples is the juice of the fiery chilli pepper (hot when green, incendiary when red!), but many are also habit-forming stimulants and some are flavour-enhancers. Some cola nuts may contain as much as 2.3 per cent caffeine.

Caffeine can cause palpitations, increase gastric secretions, act as a diuretic (increasing urine flow) and cause gastric ulcers where over-used.

The removal of caffeine is well-exploited by the makers who do not normally bother to explain what their 'flavours' contain. Nor do they bother to explain that in non-diet cola drinks, a single can may contain up to seven teaspoons of cane sugar. The conclusion? They prefer to tell you what's *not* in their products! (See pp. 138–141 on Perrier Water.) These details may also reveal why drinks-producers naturally exploit a loophole clause in the British Food Labelling Regulations – because it is there! Most choose to provide numbers or names of the substances, meaning that many consumers will not make a deductive connection between the numbers and the additives, especially where a number only is given.

Many ginger ales contain 'carbonated water, sugar, citric acid, flavourings, colour (E150) and preservative E211'. Citric acid is listed here without its E number (E330), while sulphite ammonia caramel is described as 'colour'. The preservative listed is E211 sodium benzoate, to which some drinkers, such as asthmatics and urticaria-sufferers, may be sensitive or allergic.

Bitter lemon drinks invariably contain E211 sodium benzoate, E220 sulphur dioxide, E300 ascorbic acid (vitamin C), E414 gum arabic, E104 quinoline yellow (a 'coal-tar' or azo dye – see Glossary), saccharin and quinine sulphate, an ingredient of many tonic waters.

Lemonade, far from being a simple and refreshing drink produced from squeezed lemons, often contains E331 sodium citrate (which can alter the urinary excretion of drugs from the body), E211 sodium benzoate, E466 (a derivative of cellulose), saccharin, aspartame and often E160(a) alpha carotene, an intense yellow-to-orange colouring matter.

Slimline drinks typically contain E211 and E104 (as above), E142 acid brilliant green (another 'coal-tar' dye) and aspartame or saccharin or both. One of the most apparently complicated soft drinks is cream soda, which is often described as: 'carbonated water, sugar, flavourings, lactic acid, acidity regulator, sodium benzoate, sodium saccharin, stabilizer: quillaia extract'. Some of these substances are 'natural', such as sugar and the flavourings, which are usually vanilla extracts (derived from the seed pods of a tree). Lactic acid's E number is E270, the acidity regulator is 576 (no E number allocated) sodium gluconate; sodium benzoate is E211, sodium saccharin is a familiar acquaintance (!), and quillaia extract is a 'natural' head-retaining agent derived from the bark of a South American tree.

Whether quillaia extract poses risks to drinkers depends upon how much they consume and for how long, as with most additives. The FACC listed quillaia in its (cautious) Group B in 1970, because of centuries of medical evidence that *prolonged exposure to small doses can cause gastrointestinal irritation*. By 1972 the SCF had looked at the additive, agreeing with the JECFA that the commercial product is poorly specified (i.e. its identity is often in question chemically). Following the SCF's further look at the additive in 1978, it was approved for use throughout the EEC, Britain and the USA.

The perceptive shopper strolling again among the soft drinks shelves may notice that, unlike the fruit solids in home-made squashes and juice drinks, those in manufactured drinks do not fall to the bottom of the bottle when stored. This is achieved by the use of another of the maker's 'vital' additives – E400 alginic acid, which acts as a suspending-agent.

Where cola drinks are concerned, I was heartened to see a day-glow stripe on an example, which informed potential purchasers that, 'Coca-cola now tastes even better', followed by: '100 per cent NutraSweet', which I hope does not mean that it contains nothing but aspartame, but you never know with this kind of labelling! This is an example of a marketing angle which the food producers' promotions people term 'a USP' (unique selling point). At the root of this kind of marketeer's jargon is the need to develop a product identity (or 'profile', as they prefer to call it) which will help to sell the product in the face of fierce competition. In this case, it is not difficult to estimate the growing level of drinks-marketing panic – a synthetic sweetener has become a USP!

Very few soft drinks contain genuinely 'unique' ingredients, although some contain genuinely surprising additives. One example is the famous carbonated drink based on glucose and heavily advertised as the athlete's perfect energy-restorer. Since glucose is colourless, why is the drink a resonant yellow-to-orange colour? The answer is that, as explained on the label, it contains 'colour: sunset yellow'. What a nice, colourful-sounding ingredient! It is, in fact, E110 sunset yellow FCF, a 'coal-tar' or azo dye. This is another of the synthetic colouring matters to which some people are allergic. The Hyperactive Children's Support Group have recommended that it be eliminated from the diet of children who reveal sensitivity to such synthetic colours.

The rule with soft drinks, as with all other drinks where labels are provided, is READ THE LABELS CAREFULLY BEFORE BUYING THEM, not after they have started their journey into your body.

## 'Microscopic' Labelling

– The information implosion (how not to get the message across)

Food- and drinks-manufacturers put a great deal of effort into finding new methods of fudging essential information, perhaps with the aim of evading what they see as the negative business effect of revealing the suspiciously complicated chemical nature of their liquid assets in particular.

Each month, it seems, a new technique of evasion or word-juggling is born, each move further confusing the information available to the drinker or diner.

One of the most novel is the neat little trick of positioning the legally required label of ingredients of a soft drink on the metal cap of each bottle. The typeface of this printed information is so small (about 4 pt) as to make it virtually unreadable with the naked eye. For example, half the area of a one-inch (25 mm) diameter cap on a bottle of diet Coca-Cola is taken up with the maker's logo, and the other half with a label of substances included in the drink. The ingredients are identical to those given in the canned version above, except for the inclusion of caffeine in the bottled drink.

The clear advantage for the drinks-manufacturer of this tiny list of ingredients is that in most cases the barman removes and discards the bottle cap (and its label of ingredients) well before it approaches its interface with the drinker. As a result, the prospective (young) imbiber of a soft drink containing a fair number of 'certain substances' gets no chance to find out what he is about to pour into his bloodstream, and even should he catch a glimpse of the label/cap, he would only be able to decipher the details thereon had he remembered to bring along his handy scanning electron microscope, complete with its lorry-filling power supply! Further, the 'sell-by' date is often stamped across this miniature of twentieth-century industrial art labelling, obscuring some of the ingredient details. In contrast, each of the bottles of Coca-Cola which features a throwaway cap contains a semi-permanent embossed legend in white, which the maker clearly considers important information: 'Regd. bottle device and trade mark of the Coca-Cola Company'.

A Spanish strong lager called San Miguel (og 1,047 or 5.4 per cent ABV) is provided with a 'label' on its throw-away cap, as is an Italian lager of similar strength called Nastro Azzurro. Information about these two lagers' ingredients is printed around the cap, immediately above the crimped castellations, making them the first alcoholic drinks in Europe to be so labelled. These are near-pure lagers, containing only ascorbic acid (an anti-oxidant) and carbon dioxide under pressure as listed ingredients.

# 9 Mineral Waters

Oh, plunge your hands in water, plunge them in to the wrist;
Stare, stare at the basin, and wonder what you've missed.

W.H. Auden

## Hope Springs Eternal

It may not have the decadent undertones associated with
Cleopatra and her asses' milk, but there is one form of
non-alcoholic drink which is traditionally suited to both bathing
and drinking – mineral water, or 'spa water' as it used to be
called.

The use of this (largely) unprocessed, dual-purpose fluid,
which has taken on a new lease of life in modern times, began
with the Romans. They believed that drinking and bathing in
the water which issued from natural hot springs, especially
those which provided water that was iron or sulphur-bearing,
was beneficial. As a result, the sulphur spring at Aachen,
Germany, was a favourite Roman resort, as was Bath in Britain,
still a popular resort today.

A town called Spa, near Liège, Belgium, was the first of
Europe's fashionable 'watering-places' (the term now covers
any drinking-house, alcoholic or not), and anyone who might
have been listed in the Euro version of *Who's Who* in the
sixteenth and seventeenth centuries would have visited the
baths there, when their popularity was at its peak. The
chalybeate (iron-bearing) springs at Spa had, though, been
known since the fourteenth century.

The most famous French spas were at Aix-les-Bains and
Vichy. Other famous spas existed at Bath, Cheltenham,
Harrogate, Leamington and Tunbridge Wells – all in Britain –
and well-known springs existed at Wiesbaden, Aix la Chapelle
and Baden-Baden, all in Germany, and at White Sulphur
Springs in the USA.

It must have been rather novel and very pleasant to bathe in
warm, naturally fizzy spring water – a kind of 'green' bathing

experience. The notion that mineral-spring bathers might derive general health or even curative benefits from the drinking of the bathwater continues to be promoted today. The perennial desire to be made whole is perennially exploitable!

Since mineral waters often contain relatively high amounts of iron, they may limit anaemia in drinkers. Unfortunately, the greater part of the world's under-nourished people live in Africa and India, a long way from Bath. The wealthy continue to 'take the waters', as do 'foodies' and other health-conscious, aware citizens of the West, in the form of a dozen or more bottled mineral waters from all over Europe.

Such waters contain many minerals: potassium, sodium, iron, calcium, sulphur, magnesium, cadmium and manganese. Sources are officially checked for pathogenic (harmful) organisms and radioactive elements. In the nineteenth century many bathers sought out radium-containing springs because they considered radioactive materials to be health-giving!

## Hidden Depths

Mineral waters have their origins deep underground, where, under intense heat and pressure, minerals are leeched from surrounding rocks by trapped or moving water. They are often impregnated with carbon dioxide gas, giving them natural fizz. This is the result of chemical reactions which are aided by 'boiling' in enclosed (pressurized) conditions, much like those in a car's radiator. The waters so derived are specified in EEC definitions as 'naturally carbonated natural mineral waters', as opposed to those which are aided by artificial carbonation.

As with any 'natural' drinks, such as milk, natural mineral waters are excluded from specific labelling regulations, although in Europe they must conform to standards laid down in EEC Directive 80/778/EEC,* which involves periodic inspections of sources and extraction equipment, as well as checks for pathogenic infection of the water itself.

As we have seen, there is no reason to suppose that naturally occurring substances are any more or any less dangerous than artificial substances, but the exclusion of such chemically

* Augments main directive. *See* References.

complicated drinks (see Perrier analysis, following) from labelling controls reveals once more THE GAPING HOLES IN REGULATION. Mineral waters are therefore treated similarly to alcoholic drinks, except for the detail that mineral waters-producers must provide data on request from consumers.

Some trade associations consider Indian tonic water to be a mineral water, but this is a processed concoction, containing the anti-malaria drug quinine, E330 citric acid, E211 sodium benzoate as a preservative, and either aspartame or saccharin as a sweetener.

The first of the natural mineral waters to be bottled and marketed as a drink was Vichy Water, in the seventeenth century. There are now vast international markets for French brands such as Perrier, Badoit, Volvic and the perennial Vichy, English brands such as Ashbourne, Buxton and Malvern, and from Belgium the original Spa. North of the border in Britain they bottle Highland Spring which, in its generic form, is also a strongly marketed (and listed on labels) ingredient of Baxter's Soups. Also available are Irish Spring Water and Oras from Cyprus.

Some mineral waters are artificially carbonated after being pumped from underground wells (which are bored and capped rather like oil wells), so these versions must be labelled to show the words 'carbonated'.

Both the EEC Directive and the British Natural Mineral Waters Regulations 1985 require that producers adopt one of two methods of constituent indication: either the words 'composition in accordance with the officially recognized analysis of ...' or a statement of the main mineral constituents. Producers who opt for the former are expected to provide details of the analysis on request. Many choose the former method, perhaps because they fear the negative effect upon sales of the revelation that mineral waters often contain lead, arsenic and other materials which members of the public consider to be poisonous.

Possibly the most successful of the brands is Perrier, and its analysis confirms that there is a lot more to mineral waters than $H_2O$ and flavour.

## Eau What a Lot We've Got!

Perrier's labels show the firm's well-crafted art work and (like some other brands) a small panel containing the words: 'Composition in accordance with the officially recognized analysis of 3rd November 1984.' A new sample was taken and analysed on 3rd January 1989 and during 1990 this new date is likely to appear on bottles of Perrier Water, circulating simultaneously with stocks showing the 1984 analysis date.

No matter which analysis date appears on the label, however, drinkers who want to know details of Perrier Water's composition must telephone or write to the makers in Lygon Place, London SW1 and await a copy of the analysis printout – this might be a problem if you are really thirsty.

Such prevarication leaves the consumer disadvantaged, because he or she is unlikely to pursue the matter further, unless a carefully weighed decision on the drink is contemplated. To be fair, the full composition of Perrier Water, as analysed in 1984 would have taken up most of the label:

Elements or compounds are identified with their chemical symbols, in the form in which they appoear on the drink – i.e. silicon is present as silicon dioxide ($SiO_2$)

pH – 6.0
dry residue at + 180°C 447.4 mg/l (milligrams per litre)

| | | | |
|---|---|---|---|
| Silica in | ($SiO_2$) | 12.3 | mg/l |
| Bicarbonate | ($HCO_3$) | 347.7 | mg/l |
| Chloride | (Cl) | 30.9 | mg/l |
| Sulphate | ($SO_4$) | 51.4 | mg/l |
| Nitrite in | (N) | nil | mg/l |
| Nitrate in | (N) | 3.6 | mg/l |
| Fluoride | (F) | 0.08 | mg/l |
| Cyanide | (Cn) | 0.005 | mg/l |
| Phosphate | ($PO_4$) | 0.014 | mg/l |
| Carbon Dioxide | ($CO_2$) | 6392.3 | mg/l |
| Calcium | (Ca) | 140.2 | mg/l |
| Magnesium | (Mg) | 3.5 | mg/l |
| Potassium | (K) | 1.0 | mg/l |
| Sodium | (Na) | 14.0 | mg/l |
| Lithium salts | (Li) | 0.005 | mg/l |

| Iron | (Fe) | 0.020 | mg/l |
|------|------|-------|------|
| Manganese | (Mn) | 0.01 | mg/l |
| Copper | (Cu) | 0.020 | mg/l |
| Silver | (ag) | 0.005 | mg/l |
| Barium | (Ba) | 0.005 | mg/l |
| Ammonium | (NH$_4$) | 0.05 | mg/l |
| Cadmium | (Cd) | 0.001 | mg/l |
| Chromium | (Cr) | 0.020 | mg/l |
| Lead | (Pb) | 0.001 | mg/l |
| Zinc | (Zn) | 0.020 | mg/l |
| Arsenic | (As) | 0.005 | mg/l |
| Selenium | (Se) | 0.005 | mg/l |

The presentation of details in this way is misleading. Perrier's 1984 list describes one item as 'Nitrate in N' (i.e. as nitrogen), with the figure of 3.6 mg per litre, whereas the true figure for nitrates in this sample should be given as 16 mg per litre. A test by *Which?* magazine in 1989 discovered a level of 27 mg/litre, although this is still well within official safety limits and is only half the maximum permitted level in EEC regulations for tap water.

I was sent a *full version* of the 1984 analysis from Perrier's London office within a few days of requesting it early in 1988. When I telephoned the same office in September 1989 requesting a full version of the January 1989 analysis I was told: 'Only the short version is available.' I asked that it be sent to me (it was, a few days later) and also that a full version be obtained for me. The firm's marketing manager said that it might take some time because he would have to get the details from France. I asked why the London office had no copy of the full analysis and he replied: 'Most members of the public prefer the short version. It's less complicated and is easier to understand than the full version. Normal customers don't require that level of detail,' he went on, perhaps not realizing that he was categorizing me as abnormal, but if it was a calculated insult, I ignored it.

After a four-week wait, I telephoned the marketing manager again and was told, 'Nothing has arrived.' My conclusion: the London office of a leading world company selling millions of bottles of a natural mineral water every week did not possess a copy of the water's chemical analysis, NINE MONTHS AFTER THE ANALYSIS SAMPLE WAS TAKEN.

THE 'SHORT' ANALYSIS (SAMPLE TAKEN 3 JANUARY 1989)
The new analysis of the same water, derived from Perrier's source at Vergeze, France, appears to indicate that at least ten substances shown in the 1984 list have 'disappeared'. While bicarbonates and sodium and calcium remain at about the same levels, neither ARSENIC, LEAD, FLUORIDE nor CADMIUM appear in the list of substances the water is said to contain, and the most dominant substance in the 1984 list – Le Fizz (carbon dioxide gas) – has apparently ceased to be a constituent.

Mineral waters regulations permit makers to confine descriptions of the product to the water's 'principal constituents', so Perrier are within their rights to refuse me a full analysis, but since $CO_2$ must surely remain the largest single constituent, why is it not mentioned? On the other hand it is not a 'mineral' as such, so this may represent another regulatory loophole.

Two new substances have mysteriously appeared on the list, although they are not present in the water: aluminium and hydrogen sulphide, whose levels are given as 'zero'. Why mention them if they are not constituents? Presumably the water does not contain plankton or moon rock, so why not mention these items and everything else not contained? The list would be endless. The most likely explanation for this oddity and the discrepancies between the two analyses, separated by five years, is that publicity alone has changed Perrier Water for the good! The British tabloid press tells its readers that aluminium and lead are 'bad news', so steps are taken at Perrier to ensure that these metals do not exist in the drink, for obvious marketing reasons. Nevertheless, the nitrates level has suddenly jumped to 17.5 mg/litre, this figure approaching that suggested by *Which?* in its 1989 test.

Perhaps the most important analytical question is this: how reliable can a maker's published analyses be in conveying the true chemical nature of such bottled waters? Assuming that some changes have taken place in the fluid since 1984, due to the gradual seepage of rainwater into the source, HOW MUCH HAS PERRIER WATER CHANGED AGAIN SINCE THE ANALYSIS OF JANUARY 1989? Can a difficult-to-obtain analysis which was already nine months old when the first labels might have appeared on bottles, be relied upon as accurate?

Since mineral waters do not change appreciably after bottling, 'mature' Perrier Water will continue to circulate alongside the new, apparently 'cleaner' water. If nothing else, though, this drink could continue to aid people who suffer with acid indigestion, because its pH has shifted only slightly between the two analyses: pH 6.0 in 1984, pH 5.7 in 1989.

## Vital Minerals or Chemical Hogwash?

They may appear similar to the Food Labelling Regulations in the details they exclude, but EEC and British mineral waters regulations enforce considerably more inspection and control over the drink than is exercised over soft drinks or alcoholic drinks.

Analysis of each water and its source is mandatory and maximum levels of toxic substances are laid down: arsenic 50 mg/litre, cadmium 5 mg/litre and cyanide 50 mg/litre among other minerals.

Are the minerals in such waters really of any benefit to human health? Human beings require the following principal minerals in fairly large amounts: calcium, chlorine, iron, magnesium, potassium, phosphorous and sodium. Many trace elements (also termed 'micronutrients') are necessary in the production of enzymes, which provide vital functions within cells and in creating hormones in glands. These micronutrients are: barium, bromine, chromium, cobalt, copper, fluoride, iodine, lithium, manganese, molybdenum, nickel, strontium and zinc.

Of the main minerals, iron is vital to the production of haemoglobin, which carries oxygen around the bloodstream (a deficiency causes anaemia) and calcium is needed for repair and growth of bones and teeth. Iodine is the most important of the micronutrients, being vital to thyroid gland functioning, and its effect upon growth. It is available in the normal diet in fish, sea salt and green vegetables.

Whether the drinker benefits from mineral waters is difficult to assess unless he or she is prepared to volunteer as an expendable guinea pig in a scientific trial. This might involve starvation diets, very little 'normal water', numerous blood tests and some very uncomfortable gastric experiences, risking the sort of metabolic changes which might be inclined to drive a formerly well-balanced citizen to drink! It's a matter of opinion whether mineral waters are healthy.

Morris Jacobs, writing in *Collier's Encyclopaedia* in 1983 had made up his mind as revealed when he defined natural mineral waters as: 'Those natural waters which have dissolved sufficient materials from the rocks, earth and soil through which they pass, to give them a distinctive character of their own, and to render them, in large measure, unsuitable for drinking.'

The use of natural mineral waters for curative purposes is excluded from the labelling and control regulations, which means that practically any kind of water can be offered for consumption on private premises such as nursing homes or hospitals.

A curious coincidence occurs in Bath, Avon. One of the breweries producing additive-free beer has an outlet only a stone's throw from the Mineral Water Hospital in the centre of the town. Miner's Arms beers are available in Hatchett's in Queen Street.

It is said that pubs which are close to alcoholics' 'drying out' centres are the most profitable (I wonder why?), but so far I have not heard of any comparisons between the curative powers of real ale and those of waters heavy in iron and sulphur.

# 10   Matters of Taste

Taste all and hand the knowledge down.

Gary Snyder

## Tongue Ticklers

The main distinguishing characteristic of any drink is probably its flavour. If you don't really care what a drink may be doing to you, only what it is doing *for* you, perhaps taste-satisfaction is your sole priority.

A drink loses its identity when the flavour goes or declines, and without this enjoyment factor there is only the quenching of a thirst or, in the case of an alcoholic, the relief that comes with the 'shot' of alcohol.

Taste responses are subjective. Everyone knows what a lemon tastes like, but the inadequacies of language result in common ground expressions such as 'bitter' or 'acrid' to describe it, none of which really matches the taste experience.

'There's a definite hint of loganberry there,' says the gorgeous young winetaster on television, eyelids fluttering fetchingly behind her trendy spectacles with enormous lenses. When I try the same supermarket wine there's a definite hint of a brew by Sarsons.

Seated in a classic old centre-of-London pub, I was sampling an early half-pint of beer. I was the sole occupant of the pub, it being mid-morning.

With a full 11½-hours to go, the barman was giving the bar a final wipe over when two ventricose young men squeezed through the door.

'Mornin', gents,' said the middle-aged barman.

'Morning,' said one of the two, 'we'll have a pint of Young's Bitter apiece.'

The beer was placed on the bar, and the contents of one pint glass disappeared immediately, straight down the hatch.

'Lovely,' said the thirsty bloke. 'Fill 'er up again.'

'Pay up first,' said the wary barman.

The two men looked at each other. The very thirsty one said: 'Do we get a discount, cos we're your official CAMRA tasters?'

The barman's response was unprintable.

He came over to my table as the two young men, a little crestfallen, retired to a far corner of the bar.

'They think they invented real ale, don't they,' he ventured.

I replied, cautiously: 'There's something in what you say.'

He went on: 'They did their bit in the early seventies to get the stuff back on the road, but now they seem to think the landlords should pay them back with cheap beer, via their so-called "tasting panels". Anyone knows that one person's taste never matches another's.'

Quite! I said I had doubts about these gentlemen's credentials and that CAMRA don't make use of 'lay drinkers' on their tasting panels – only 'experts' (whose taste is also subjective). These gents were clearly public bar opportunists, with no official connection with CAMRA, but it was clear that they liked their real ale.

Strength of flavour in drinks is due to several factors, including unfermented or modified matter remaining, such as isobutanol (an alcohol) and the amount of volatile esters they contain. The latter substances are vaporized when heated, or released into the air by natural means, as when an orange is broken open, for example. Esters, some of which are complex alcohols, are responsible for the aroma of both food and drink (*see* Glossary: ester).

Dry hops add volatile esters to real ale, accounting for the drink's much stronger aroma compared with lager or stout, while the 'nose' of a good wine is created and preserved by the careful selection of grapes and cautious maturation respectively.

Esters are flavour-enhancers but, unlike monosodium glutamate, a synthetic enhancer which is often added to processed foods, their existence in drinks arises from natural constituents, although this is not necessarily true of keg lager, which is often given additional aroma by the use of esters contained in concentrated syrups called 'spicy' and 'floral' hop extracts, which are sometimes added after lagering.

One much-used ester, E405 propylene glycol alginate, however, is not used for its flavour-boosting properties, but for cosmetic reasons. See Appendix 2.

## Le Saucerie

Between friends, differences in taste or opinion are irritating in direct proportion to their triviality.

W.H. Auden

Chefs all over the world know of the flavour-boosting properties of esters, even if they are not aware of their existence, except as active elements of various spices and herbs. In France and Italy they know how to use garlic and other fresh herbs to this end, while the Indian chef employs a wide range of seeds and leaves of plants such as coriander (also called 'Chinese parsley') and fenugreek, added to the dish just before serving and creating powerful and appetizing aroma at the table. Conventional 'Western' dishes, such as steak in a cream-and-brandy sauce, depend upon esters in their main ingredients, with peppercorns adding the taste-stimulating aroma in steak *au poivre*, for example.

None of these effects would pay off for the chef, however, were it not for the high accuracy sensing process carried on by aroma-receptors in the diner's or drinker's nose, and the taste-buds on the tongue. Taste-buds have a remarkable capacity to test, sense and pass on information to the brain at the speed of light.

As well as being one of the body's most powerful pleasure-inducing functions, this food-sensing (smelling) ability (described by food standards inspectors as an 'organoleptic function') helps to prevent the intake of decaying or poisonous matter.

Aroma in wine is important. Try sniffing a bottle of plonk and comparing it with a good Spanish Rioja. You pay for the difference. In the taste stakes, alcoholic drinks-manufacturers have a built-in advantage: alcohol, and especially butyl alcohol (isobutanol), acts upon the taste-bud nerve-endings, increasing the sensation of taste, a phenomenon brought into play by aperitif wines, which are sipped just before a meal.

Alcohol's taste-enhancing effect explains its appeal in thousands of flavour combinations throughout the world – the world of drinks.

## Drinkers' Delusions (common myths and fallacies)

Alcoholic drinks are often invested, by both the learned and the ill-informed, with curative and life-enhancing properties. Some of these myths and fallacies have a foundation in fact, while others are the result of time spent on marketing-ploys by the 'romantic fiction' personnel in the big drinks-producers' publicity departments.

*'The drinking of alcohol prevents or cures many diseases.'*
This fallacy may well have been generated by one of the inveterate boozers whom former *Punch* columnist Thomas Jay once described as 'the old soaks at home'. Whoever it was, though, was mistaken, because in some ways the drinking of alcohol is more likely to reduce resistance to disease by affecting the immune system, although this occurs only in the later stages of alcoholism. It is a convenient fallacy for a confirmed and willing drinker to promote, and its only (tenuous) link with fact lies in the use of alcohol as an external bactericide. When pure alcohol is used to swab part of a human being's skin, bacteria which might find their way into the body through an abrasion or the injection of a hypodermic are destroyed. It is thus used generally in hospitals for pre-injection sterilization.

*'Being light in colour and flavour, lager is the least fattening of drinks.'*
The calorie-count of ale, stout and lager is identical, strength for strength, and is set by the amount of unfermented material left in the fluid after brewing, added to the calorific value of the alcohol it contains. Ounce for ounce, alcohol is considerably more fattening than starch (carbohydrate), making the strength of a drink calorifically more important than any other characteristic. The ability to fatten is enhanced in strong, sweet ales, which may be one source of the fallacy, but the most likely explanation is that it was the result of a story circulated in the early years of lager-promotion, intended to spread the word about the health 'advantages' of the pale yellow beer. You only have to look at a few of your lager-drinking friends to realize that, from the side, they are indistinguishable from your ale- or stout-drinking friends. The so-called 'long drinks' (beer and cider) carry more overall calories than wines or spirits, due to

their high starch-content, but liqueurs are the most fattening. It really all depends upon how much you drink.

### 'Port-drinking causes gout'

Many years of illustrations in humorous magazines, showing a ripe old ex-military officer with a bulbous nose and a foot grotesquely wrapped in bandages or plaster, have maintained this myth in excellent condition for many years.

Gout is an inherited condition which can affect the knees, tendons, ears, elbows, hands and feet, and is caused by the development of uric acid crystals in the joints. The condition normally affects men aged from twenty to sixty and seldom affects women. It is not triggered by drinking port (or lager!), although some doctors believe there is a link between its onset and heavy drinking or some other element of diet. Currently, work is proceeding which tends to suggest that the complaint is due to an allergic response, just as some people are allergic to sulphur dioxide and to gluten in wheatflour. However, the complaint is very painful, and a bottle of port occasionally might bring a little relief!

### 'Stout such as Guinness contains large quantities of iron, so is very good for you.'

In spite of numerous tests over the years, nobody has yet managed to find any more iron in stout than in any other beer. For many years after the Second World War, stout-drinking declined in Britain, as did brown ale-drinking in the 1970s. It may be that the highly creative Guinness advertising team introduced this idea – remember the toucan ads with the slogan 'My goodness, my Guinness'? Another possibility is that, with advancing years, some men graduate to a drier taste in their beer, perhaps due to declining taste-bud sensitivity. With the higher probability that they will become hospitalized, what better psychological reinforcement could a doctor give than to prescribe 'two bottles of stout per day'? Stout is brewed from a blend of chocolate malt grains, black malt grains, pale malt and roasted barley and contains no more (nor less) iron than best bitter or lager.

### 'The hair-of-the-dog cure is the most effective hangover treatment.'

Taking 'the hair of the dog that bit you' is an old English superstition based upon an even older (Roman) one which asserted that, if bitten by a dog, one would be cured by consuming one of the dog's hairs. Some drinkers swear by the technique, which involves one or two drinks the following morning, just as the hangover becomes really apparent in all its day-wrecking horror. It is probably true that it has a temporary effect, due to the 'shrunken' brain cells which cause the headache becoming temporarily relaxed by the new 'injection' of alcohol, but most people report a far more severe hangover later in the same day, when this effect has worn off. The only cures for a hangover are time and abstinence.

Hair-of-the-dog 'cures', which often contain alcohol in hidden mixtures, are potentially dangerous for the moderate drinker, because they may increase his or her tolerance of alcohol, leading to higher and higher intakes, in order to achieve the same 'effect'. This is a likely route to addiction.

*'Long drinks such as lager and cider are less dangerous than wine or spirits.'*
Whether you drink wine, sherry, whisky, beer or cider will have little effect upon the way in which your body deals with the effects of alcohol. Acetaldehyde is formed in the body as a result of consuming alcohol and, depending upon the amount each drinker's body produces (there are many variable factors) of this so-called 'super-toxin', so one suffers more or less from undesirable effects. Oriental peoples suffer less from alcoholism and alcohol dependence than people in the Western world, due to an instant reaction in some individuals, who break out in a rash. It is thought that the variation in reactions may be due to differing genetic factors, but in general the type of drink consumed is relatively unimportant. The quantity of alcohol in drinks is all that matters to your liver, brain and sex organs, which may be damaged by over-indulgence. Damage can also occur to the digestive tract, although beer and cider are probably less damaging in this respect than wine or spirits. The lining of the stomach is highly sensitive to irritant substances such as alcohol, and although a protective mucous may be excreted initially when imbibing spirit drinks, there is evidence to suggest that regular spirit-drinking may increase the likelihood of developing duodenal ulcers or oesophagal (gullet) cancers; however, the highest incidence of such fatal cancers occurs in the major wine-drinking nations of France, Germany, Spain and Italy.

It is not necessarily true that the stronger (spirit) drinks are more quickly assimilated, unless 'chasing' is embarked upon. This is because the pylorus or pyloric sphincter reacts to strong drinks by shutting off the outlet to the stomach where, eventually, about eighty per cent of the alcohol will be absorbed. It follows that there is an optimum strength of drink which will just fail to trigger this spasm, encouraging swift inebriation; that level is AROUND 20 PER CENT BY VOLUME, the average concentration of a spirit chased by a lager or cider. This factor explains the powerful hangovers generated by drinks which are at that alcohol concentration, such as port (22–25 per cent) or sherry (17–20 per cent). All these risks can be minimized (and some doctors would say eliminated) by adhering to safe drinking-levels and habits.

*'DTs (delirium tremens) is a sequence of hallucinations brought on by consuming too much alcohol at one session.'*
It is an odd fact that the majority of cases of DTs occur in people who have just been arrested or admitted to hospital. The reason for this unhappy relationship is that delirium tremens is not, as is generally supposed, an immediate consequence of over-indulgence but a withdrawal symptom experienced by an alcoholic who has suddenly become unable to obtain any alcohol. Symptoms include severe hallucinations and intermittent coma, the effects of shock on the brain sometimes resulting in death. In some cases, however, the delirium is self-limiting and may stop after a few days. These cases can be aided by injections of vitamin $B_1$, which is often deficient due to poor diet or sudden loss of appetite. DTs, which are an acute symptom of alcoholism, should not be confused with 'the shakes', a general feeling of nervousness and internal 'jitter' which can result from simple over-indulgence.

*'Genuine real ale can only be brewed from true English hops, such as Goldings.'*
A good deal of fiction, masquerading as 'astonishing and interesting facts about beer', is generated by the specialist home-brewing press and the Sunday newspaper glossy magazines. One of these stories enthused about the unique Englishness of certain hops, most of the tale being filled out with romantic names and fake rural images of Olde England. An item

in one of the Sunday glossies, entitled 'The Perfect Pint', referred to 'Kentish Goldings' being used in a commercial beer, as though they were a special and secret ingredient, details of which are revealed only to the inner circle of trendy food- and drink-writers and columnists. Now I have heard of the 'man of Kent' (born east of the Medway river) and his opposite number 'Kentish man' (born west of the Medway), but should I choose to invent a new name for a mythical variety of hops, I would try to get my geographical orientation correct for a start. The famous Goldings are grouped under a common term for the indigenous product – East Kent Goldings (EKG universally) – but if I wanted a brand new name for an imaginative item in a newspaper, I would prefer to select the accurate description 'Goldings of Kent' to conform to the easterly drift. Goldings come from every corner of the world – Styrian Goldings come from Yugoslavia, for example – and even those from East Kent are often tagged by their varietal names, such as Golding Clusters (once grown near my home in Farnham), Early Goldings and Hill Goldings, the latter variety also having once been grown in Hampshire. Real ale can be made from any hops, and German hops produce excellent top-fermented brews. Hallertau is the dominant hop in Germany. Glenny Brewery of Witney, Oxon, brews a bitter ale using Hallertau hops.

*'Drinking is a good cure for insomnia.'*
Alcohol is a hypnotic substance, which means that its principal effect, like that of sleeping-pills, is depression of the nervous system. Drinking fairly heavily may make you feel sleepy and therefore may help you to get to sleep, but the inability to sleep without having a drink could indicate increasing dependence on alcohol. Furthermore, although after a heavy drinking session you may fall asleep immediately, the irritant effect of the alcohol upon the drinker's brain cells will almost certainly bring wakefulness within a few hours, causing the night's sleep to be fractious and disturbed. Alcohol-dependent drinkers suffer the twin effects of insomnia when they do not drink, and shallow sleep when they do. If you need to drink alcohol every day, you are almost certainly alcohol-dependent.

*'Winemaking, brewing and distilling are highly scientific undertakings which cannot be carried on effectively by amateurs.'*
While facilities such as laboratories and a staff of analytical

chemists and microbiologists might enable a large drinks-concern to control the flavour and colour of one or all of its products to close limits, scientific prowess is in general irrelevant to the production of healthy drinks. The 'high technology' fallacy is used by some producers to deflect questions from members of the public about their ingredients and recipes. Drinks-production employs only basic scientific skills in its additive-free forms but becomes more complex where the use of preservatives and other additives is concerned, meaning that the process is deliberately converted into a high-technology undertaking in order to boost profits. In its pure drinks form, the process is akin to culinary skills or agriculture, exploiting methods of plant growth (i.e. yeast) in a variety of culture media, rather like yogurt-making in the kitchen. There is no reason why anyone who is capable of following a recipe should not be able to produce excellent wine or beer consistently, with a minimum of plant, on a kitchen table.

*'The sediment in naturally conditioned beer gives you diarrhoea.'*
The 'sediment' is simply yeast in bottled natural beers such as Guinness or Worthington White Shield pale ale, and it is more likely that the alcohol-content added to unfermented malts in the drink would induce stomach or bowel problems, but even then, only on an empty stomach. Yeast-Vite and other dried yeast pharmaceutical preparations contain exactly the same material (the yeast is simply dried and pelleted), but drinkers do not make such claims concerning them. If strong ales cause such obvious symptoms, a drinker should clearly stick to weaker versions.

*'Green mould on top of a bottle's cork is a sure sign of a well-aged wine.'*
The classy image of wine has been responsible for as many faked fluids as the faked *objets d'art* found in antique shops. Where an 'age-old mould' is concerned, it is simplicity itself to grow a convincing sample on a wine-bottle cork. The winemaker simply inverts the wine for a few weeks after bottling, causing a little wine to seep through the cork, which is porous to fluid but not to air. Wild fungus organisms (yeasts) and bacteria in the air feed on the seeped wine, and within a few weeks, if the weather is warm, a green mould grows on top of the cork, in some cases under the shrunk-on plastic or lead cork cover. A few winemakers extend the 'well-aged' look by dripping soiled candlewax down the bottle's side. The greenest (most gullible) aspect of wine is often the drinker!

*'Cola drinks have never contained cocaine, only cocoa extracts.'*
With the increasingly bad press which the highly concentrated
form of cocaine called Crack is receiving, the makers of cola
drinks have redoubled their efforts to kill the century-old story
that these drinks once contained the drug. The confusion over
the two vastly different substances, coca and cocoa, has helped to
fudge the details, which are that in the late nineteenth and early
twentieth centuries many items of confectionery and drinks
contained small quantities of cocaine. It was considered
stimulating and mind-clearing! Cocaine is derived from the
leaves of the coca bush, which is indigenous to the Andes, where
local people chew the leaves to produce the well-known effects.
Like caffeine, a similar alkaloid stimulant found in coffee and
the cola nut, from which cola drinks are prepared, cocaine has a
marked effect upon animals, i.e. human consumers. Shortly after
being taken, cocaine produces a short period of euphoria,
alertness of mind and the apparent capacity to recover totally
from fatigue. When these effects wear off, the consumer feels
depressed and ill, which dictates the need for more and leads to
addiction. In the USA many drinks contained cocaine until
Congress passed the Pure Food and Drug Act in 1906, outlawing
the use of the habit-forming drug in foods or food products. Since
that time, the story that cola drinks contain cocaine has been
'worked on' by some of the producers, who now claim that other
alkaloids (i.e. not cocaine itself) were extracted from coca for use
in their products. Until the Act of 1906 therefore, many cola
drinks were cocktails of alkaloid stimulants. In this case the
public 'myth' steers very close to the truth.

*'Diet-style drinks help the drinker to lose weight.'*
Amateur food-descriptions analysts (there aren't any
professionals) can have nothing but admiration for the expert
way in which food-producers exploit public misconceptions and
buyer psychology. Conversely, they can have nothing but
contempt for the officials who framed the (British) Food
Labelling Regulations 1984, in such a way that manufacturers
can easily recognize and take advantage of loopholes. You
might expect that Schedule 7 of the regulations, headed
'Misleading Descriptions', would itemize classic examples of the
misleading labeller's art, but not so. Where dietary matters are
concerned, the regulation-writers forgot, ignored or had never
heard of the popular and mistaken public definition of the word

'diet'. Millions of people believe that it means 'a method of reducing weight by selecting certain foods' or 'an intake of foods which will not increase weight'. The true gastronomic meaning of 'diet' is not related to weight-loss or increase but to a general (or daily) regime of food intake. All living creatures have a certain diet: human beings pursue an omnivorous diet, lions a carnivorous diet, many birds an insectivorous diet, and so on, but the only terms banned from use in this context in the labelling regulations (except where the terms apply to a closely defined regime) are 'dietary' and 'dietetic'. Producers can therefore use the terms 'diet lemonade' or 'low-calorie diet drink' with impunity. So-called low-calorie 'diet' drinks do not reduce weight. They may not increase it appreciably, but where non-'diet' (sugar-sweetened) drinks are also drunk, the number of additives consumed may increase proportionately, depending upon choice of drinks. In such cases, since all 'diet' drinks are sweetened artificially, mainly by aspartame or saccharin, drinkers are simply adding to or altering the balance of natural/artificial sweeteners in the diet. Only years of research could determine the physiological outcome of such soft drink 'additive cocktail-shaking' in drinkers.

The typical chemicals mixture from which the cocktail is formed consists of:

'Diet' soft drinks: cola nut alkaloids (mainly caffeine), sulphite ammonia caramel, phosphoric acid, benzoic acid or sodium benzoate, aspartame or saccharin, citric acid.

Non-'diet' soft drinks: cola nut alkaloids (cola drinks only), sugar, citric acid, sulphur dioxide, gum arabic, quinoline yellow (an azo or 'coal-tar' dye), quinine sulphate.

Curiously, few soft-drinks consumers have asked the obvious question: 'Why do producers continue to make and promote non-"diet" drinks if "diet" drinks are the best thing since sliced coca leaves?' The answer is that makers are at pains to ensure that the question is suppressed, by maintaining a 'two-tiers to your choice of drinks' approach. It is sobering(!) to consider what would happen to a consumer who confined his or her diet to 'diet' drinks alone – rapid loss of weight, accompanied by loss of life within a few weeks, due to starvation.

# 11 Controlling Forces

## The Men (and the Women) from the Ministry

The Food Additives and Contaminants Committee (FACC) was formed in 1960 from a sub-committee of the Food Standards Committee (FSC), which in turn had been set up in 1947 'to advise government on the composition, description, labelling and advertising of food'. The FSC reported to both the Ministry of Food and the Ministry of Health.

As well as its report on beer in 1978, the FACC produced, up to 1984, thirty-nine reports on various topics, such as lead in food (1975) and sorbic acid (1977), the latter additive being a major processing aid in wine and a common constituent of home winemaking kits.

In 1979 the FACC produced an interim Report on the Review of Colouring Matter in Food Regulations 1973, not completing the review until October 1987.

Eight members of the FSC and seven members of the FACC were brought together to form the Food Advisory Committee (FAC) in 1983, the two former committees then being disbanded. The FAC underwent re-formation again in November 1986 and still consists of fifteen members.

In itemizing details of the individuals who comprised the FACC in 1978 and who produced the Review of Additives and Processing Aids used in the Production of Beer, I do not mean to imply that any of their links with manufacturers due to employment or funding was, or is, in any way dishonest.

## The People of the FACC

Key: C79 – also served on Interim Report on Colouring Matter in Food Regulations 1973 (report dated 1979)

C87 – also served on Final Report on Colouring Matter in Food Regulations 1973 (report dated October 1987)

Chairman: Professor Basil Weedon: FACC 1968–83. Vice-Chancellor Nottingham University

Robert Beedham: Former employee, Smedley Foods (chief chemist)

Dr Peter Brignell: (Employee ICI) (manager of corporate intelligence) C87

Dr Janet Cockroft: C79

Dr William Elstow: Manager, Weston Research Laboratories (Associated British Foods). Served on FAC 1983–5. C87

Dr W.C. Fulton: Employee Unilever (senior technical member, Food and Drink Co-ordinating Committee).

A.J. Harrison: C79

Professor I. Macdonald: Chief Medical Officer, Scottish Home and Health Department.

Dr Donald McClaren: Reader, Department of Medicine, Royal Infirmary, Edinburgh.

Professor John Norris. Director of research, Cadbury Schweppes. Adviser, British Food Manufacturing Industries Research Association (co-ordinating committee). C79

Professor Denis Parke: Department of Biochemistry, University of Surrey, Guildford. Former employee of Glaxo (1949). Research funding by British American Tobacco (BAT) 1979–85. C79

William Price-Davies: Former managing director, Cadbury Schweppes and former director of Concentrates and Essences Division, and chairman of Soft Drinks section. C79

R. Sawyer: Former Government Chemist. C79

Professor Patricia Scott: Department of Nutrition and Physiology, Royal Free Hospital. Former treasurer of Nutrition Society.

Professor Paul Turner: Department of Clinical Pharmacology, Barts Hospital. Chairman of DHSS Committee on Toxicity (COT). Research funding by ICI agrichemicals (mid-1970s) and Hoechst agrichemicals (late 1970s). Currently (1990) serving on FAC.

The food advisory committees are officially described as 'an independent body of experts'.

OTHER BODIES:

ARC/MRC           AgricultureResearchCouncil/MedicalResearch Council

| BIBRA | British Industrial Biological Research Association* |
| BNF | British Nutrition Foundation (funded by the food industry) |
| COMA | Committee on Medical Aspects of Food Policy |
| JECFA | Joint Expert Committee on Food Additives |
| NACNE | National Advisory Committee on Nutrition Education |
| SCF | Scientific Committee for Food |

* BIBRA is responsible for most of the testing of additives to food, in Britain, using laboratory animals as test subjects.

## Enzymes as Residue

It is well known that enzymes are highly reactive substances, and their comparatively recent identification in scientific terms means that little is known about any possible long-term effects of ingesting those which are added to food. Nevertheless, in addition to those provisionally approved in its report of 1978, the committee also approved the continued use of several such substances in brewing. These enzymes are used as chill-filtering agents or in a proteolytic capacity (protein-breaking) in order to prevent haze-formation during storage. All such enzymes therefore remain in the finished beer and are consumed by the drinker.

The full list of enzymes available to the brewer is:

| ∝ Amylase | The committee called for a ninety-day oral toxicity study to be carried out within two years as a condition of its approval. |
| Beta Glucanase | The committee recommended that a ninety-day feeding study be carried out in the rat with enzyme preparations derived from both Aspergillus niger and Penicillium emersonii. The committee also called for further information on the levels of residue in the final product. |
| Bromelain Glucoamylase | The committee commented that, 'There are insufficient data relating to the preparations of glucoamylase obtained from Aspergillus awamori and Rhizopus |

| | niveus, for an evaluation of safety-in-use to be made.' |
| Ficin | The committee called for a ninety-day oral toxicity study in the rat as a condition of approval. |
| Papain | This substance is derived from the fruit of the Carica papaya (pawpaw). |
| Pepsin | This enzyme is also a constituent of human saliva. |

## Other Processing Aids

Tannic acid is used as an auxiliary fining agent, as is stabilized aqueous silica solution and Lucilite, which is silica hydrogel. Perlite is also a silica-based fining agent. Glucoamylase is used principally to produce low molecular weight carbohydrates in beer, by breaking down residual dextrins. It is therefore especially suited to the production of low-carbohydrate 'diabetic' ales or lagers or low-alcohol beers of all forms. Kieselgühr and bentonite are refined clays used as fining agents.

Note: The use of enzymes, gibberellic acid, isinglass finings, perlite, polyvinylpolypyrrolidone and yeast nutrients in food is not subject to control by specific regulations.

In preparing the Report on the Review of Additives and Processing Aids used in the Production of Beer (1978), the FACC had a very difficult task. Its members were charged with the responsibility of determining the likely toxicity of many of the substances in use in large-scale brewing, and yet they had to bear in mind the possible negative effects upon the industry – in particular, effects upon the employment of the 80,000 people who work within it – of an unfavourable conclusion.

The report which emerged was, due to these influences, a well-written and detailed essay which recommended caution in the use of additives and processing aids and made few inroads into the structure of basic processes in established brewing practice in Britain.

Most of the substances submitted to and considered by the committee were approved for continued use, which must have been a great relief to some of the major suppliers of additives, such as Alginate Industries Ltd and ICI.

The report also points to the level of inertia in the brewing industry, which clearly spends a great deal of money on additives. For commercial reasons, it is probably not now possible for the big brewing combines to return to traditional, less technical methods employing few, if any, additives – there is far to much at stake.

These factors may also explain why the tests on E405 propylene glycol alginate first called for by the Pharmacology Committee in 1966 were not completed.

# Appendix 1: Regulation of Additives

## 'Suitable Additives'

In its Report on the Review of Additives and Processing Aids used in the Production of Beer (1978), the FACC (Food Additives and Contaminants Committee) approved for continued use in British brewing the following substances, which it concluded were 'suitable for food use'.

Substances which leave a residue in the final product are marked with an asterisk.

* acacia (gum arabic) E414
* acetic acid E260
* agar (carrageen) E406
* ammonia caramel E150(c)
* bentonite 558
* benzoic acid and its sodium, potassium and calcium salts – sodium benzoate E211, potassium benzoate E212 and calcium benzoate E213. Total of four permitted additives.
* bromelain
calcium bicarbonate E170
* calcium bromate
* calcium chloride 509
* calcium hydroxide 526
* calcium sulphate 516
* carrageenan E407
cellulose powder E460(ii)
citric acid E330
* dimethylpolysiloxane 900
* ethyl 4 – hydroxybenzoate E214 and its sodium salt (two additives)
* furcellaran E408
* gibberellic acid
* glucoamylase (only that derived from Bacillus subtilis and Aspergillus niger)
* hydrochloric acid 507
* hydrogen peroxide
* isinglass finings
* kieselgühr
* lactic acid E270

* L-ascorbic acid (vitamin C) E300
lucilite
* magnesium sulphate 518
* microbial proteinases (only those from Bacillus subtilis and Bacillus licheniformus)
* methyl 4 – hydroxybenzoate E218 and its sodium salt (total of two additives)
* papain
* pepsin
perlite
* phosphoric acid E338
* polyvinylpolypyrrolidone
* potassium bromate 924
potassium chloride 508
* potassium bisulphate
* propyl 4 – hydroxybenzoate E216 and its sodium salt (total of two additives)
* sodium alginate (Irish Moss) E401
* sodium bromate
sodium carbonate 500
* sodium hydroxide 524
sodium hypochlorite
* sodium sulphate 514
stabilized aqueous silica solution
* sulphur dioxide E220 and derivatives sodium sulphite E221, sodium hydrogen sulphite E222, sodium metabisulphite E223, potassium metabisulphite E224, calcium sulphite E226 and calcium hydrogen sulphite E227 (total of seven additives)
* sulphuric acid 513
* tannic acid
* yeast nutrients – mainly zinc sulphate, ferrous sulphate, copper sulphate, ammonium chloride, ammonium sulphate and B complex vitamins

In its Group B, which the committee defined as 'Substances that on the available evidence may be regarded meantime as provisionally acceptable for use in food, but about which further information is necessary and which must be reviewed within a specified period of time', were placed the two following substances:
* propane-1, 2-diol alginate (propylene glycol alginate) E405
* ∝ amylase derived from Bacillus subtilis, Aspergillus niger and Aspergillus oryzae

In its Group E, which the committee defined as 'Substances for which the available evidence was inadequate to enable an opinion to be expressed as to their suitability for use in food', were placed the following substances:
* ficin
* beta glucanase derived from Aspergillus niger and Penicillium emersonii

* glucoamylase derived from Aspergillus awamori and Rhizopus niveus
* microbial proteinases derived from Aspergillus niger, Aspergillus oryzae and Bacillus thermoproteolyticus.

Note: Ficin is an inedible material obtained from the latex of trees of the genus Ficus. It is used as a chill-proofing (chill-filtering) agent and is insoluble in water.

The committee did not place any of the substances submitted to it in either its Group C – '... possible toxicity and which ought not to be allowed in food without further evidence establishing their acceptability', or its Group D – 'Substances for which the available evidence suggests probable toxicity and which ought not to be allowed in food'.

THE COMMITTEE'S NOTES ON HEADING-AGENT E405
Alongside its general recommendations, the FACC commented on propylene glycol alginate E405 and the use of asbestos filters in brewing:

> The pharmacology Committee considered the use of propane-1, 2-diol alginate in 1966. They recommended that experiments should be carried out with the aim of determining a no-effect level in the mouse and rat. This work has not been carried out. It was noted that recent autoradiographic studies in animals indicated that this compound was hydrolised in vivo and therefore it is necessary to consider propane-1, 2-diol alginate also in terms of its components, propane-1, 2-diol alginate and alginic acid. We were concerned that propylene oxide was used in the preparation of propane-1, 2-diol alginate since residues of this epoxide in food are undesirable. A suitable specification to limit this contaminant is necessary. We recommend that a level up to 100 mg propane-1, 2-diol alginate per litre may be used in the production of beer pending the receipt within five years of the information requested by the Pharmacology Sub-Committee.

This 'information requested', amounting to results of any NEL (No Effect Level) tests on rats, with E405 as the test medium, was therefore called for by the FACC in 1966, 1970 and 1978.

The heading-agent was first introduced as a processing aid in brewing in 1960 in the USA, giving twenty-eight years in which to carry out tests for long-term carcinogenicity or mutagenicity.

## Asbestos Filters and Other Filtering Materials

In its report of 1978, the FACC commented on asbestos filters to the effect that they were:

... aware of the biological properties of asbestos in animals and man and of the evidence which suggests that the fibrous nature of this mineral is, in part, responsible for these properties. There is no evidence to suggest that the residual levels of asbestos fibres in beer would present a health hazard to the consumer. We are also told that the number of asbestos fibres is often greater in beer before filtration through an asbestos filter* than after. It is our view, however, that if a suitable alternative filter can be used, the use of asbestos filters should be phased out. Because it is likely that the biological properties of asbestos are related to its physical structure, information has been requested on the possible fibrous nature of some of the other filtration aids submitted for our opinion, namely cellulose powder and the silicates.

That a committee of noted scientists and academics should accept the word of commercial brewers, clearly brewers with a vested interest, that asbestos fibres are virtually a 'natural' constituent of beer seems extraordinary. That they should accept this opinion without calling for tests is incredible, especially bearing in mind the Food Advisory Committee's comments in their report on colouring matters in food that, 'The safety of any food ingredient, be it natural or synthetic, can only be judged from appropriate toxicology studies and any human data that may be available.'

The language of the 1978 report points to the purely advisory nature of the committee, which appears to have had no power to enforce toxicity testing. Further – and this seems remarkable coming from a body of scientists normally accustomed to linguistic precision – the term 'biological properties' is used as a euphemism for 'cancer-producing', presumably in order to block any emotive reactions in the general public to this term.

---

* Asbestos in water supplies is due to pick-up from asbestos/concrete-composition supply pipes which are being exchanged for toughened PTFE or polythene forms by most water companies.

# Appendix 2: Major Omissions

What you are drinking – the nature of the substances behind the missing numbers. Listed are the principal additives to drinks. With the exception of those additives which are also used in soft drinks (and whose names must therefore be shown on the bottle or can), none of these substances is shown on full-strength alcoholic drinks. For the full list of permitted additives to beer, see Appendix 1.

> Note: An additive with an E prefix is one which has been approved by the EEC Commission for use throughout member states. Those additives with a number only or which are described generically are approved by nationally-based committees such as the FAC and CoT. These committees report to MAFF in Britain. There is, however, a consensus among food technologists and advisory committees worldwide on the relationship between the numbers and the substances. An additive with an E prefix *is not necessarily safer than one without*.

E120 *cochineal*
A colouring matter produced by extracting the red body material of pregnant scale insects of the species Coccus cacti, found especially in South America. These insects feed and multiply on cacti and are obtained from Algiers, the Canaries, Honduras and Peru. The extract derived from their bodies contains about ten per cent carminic acid, and the colouring material is permitted in all alcoholic drinks, although it is used mainly in red wines and soft drinks in its form as ammonium carmine, which is water-soluble. Long-term carcinogenicity tests on rats with this colour revealed no adverse effects.

E150 *sulphite ammonia caramel*
Prepared by the controlled heat treatment of carbohydrates (usually glucose) with ammonia and sulphite-containing caramels. This colouring matter is used mainly in cola-type soft drinks and vinegar, although some home-brewing beer kits list E150 as an ingredient. This may be due to producers' unfamiliarity with the different types of caramel available or the tendency to give as little information as possible. Low- and no-alcohol ales and lagers may also be listed to show E150, but this is more likely to be E150(c) ammonia caramel. A CAMRA report on low-alcohol beers specified 'Caramel E150' as one of the 'nastiest

additives', perhaps themselves being unaware of the different forms of the material.

### E150(a) *plain (spirit) caramel*
Prepared by the controlled heat treatment of carbohydrates (usually glucose), either with or without an alkali or an acid. This caramel is available to drinks-producers, and tests have revealed no toxicological problems, but it is probably the least used of all the 'industrial' caramel colours.

### E150(b) *caustic sulphite caramel*
Prepared by the controlled heat treatment of carbohydrates (usually glucose) with sulphur dioxide or sulphur containing compounds. The use of this colour is confined mainly to whisky and brandy.

### E150(c) *ammonia caramel*
Produced by the controlled heat treatment of carbohydrates (usually glucose) with ammonia, and used extensively in brewing and winemaking, particularly in mild and bitter ales, some stouts and strong ales and red wine. Rats given ammonia caramel in their food and water developed lymphocytopenia, causing a fall in white blood-cell count, although when sufficient amounts of vitamin $B_6$ were given to them, this effect was reversed. So far, no experiments to observe possible similar effects upon human beings have been conducted. The FAC has set an ADI of a maximum of 100 mg per kilo of body weight in relation to both ammonia caramel and sulphite ammonia caramel, and in its Final Report on the Review of Colouring Matter in Food Regulations 1973 (first published in 1987) the committee noted that new specifications on caramels issued by the manufacturers made it difficult to decide which additive was the safest in use. Natural caramel (burnt sugar) is now rarely used. E150(c) is favoured by brewers because it does not react adversely with clarifying agents such as isinglass.

### E160(b) *annatto (also known as bixin or norbixin)*
This is a vegetable dye ranging in colour from yellow to peach or red, derived from the seed coat of the tropical tree Bixa orellana. The seeds are prickly and similar in appearance to those of the British sweet chestnut tree. The principal colouring matter is Bixin, which is extracted individually by means of organic solvents such as acetone or methanol, while the composite colour annatto, is extracted by mechanical abrasion of the seed coats. Bixin may be further processed by means of an aqueous alkali to create Norbixin. This divergence in extraction methods results in annatto's being considered a 'natural' colour, while bixin is considered a 'synthetic' colour. Annatto is used mainly as a colourant in liqueurs and soft drinks. Available data concerning effects of annatto on drinkers is sparse but includes reports that some people may be allergic to the additive. This additive is also used in some pre-cooked ('chill') foods and ready meals and kippers.

### E200 *sorbic acid*

Although this additive occurs naturally in some fruits, such as the berries of the mountain ash tree, it is mainly manufactured synthetically from ketene. Its use in wine provides a double function for the producer, because it can adjust pH level and act as a selective fungicide, destroying yeasts between the pH range 4–6, i.e. wild yeasts and beer yeasts, thus ensuring there is no 'mixing of breeds'. It is often an ingredient of home winemaking kits and is a possible skin-irritant when directly applied.

### E202 *potassium sorbate*

Manufactured from sorbic acid in the presence of potassium hydroxide, this substance 'doubles' for the effects of sorbic acid in wine but is more soluble in water. Like sorbic acid, it is often included as an ingredient of home winemaking kits and also functions as an anti-fungal (preservative) in wine in the bottle. No adverse effects are known.

### E210 *benzoic acid*

This substance occurs naturally in berries and vegetables, but it is manufactured by chemical synthesis in its commercial form. It is used in many drinks, and especially soft drinks, as an anti-fungal and anti-bacterial agent. The sodium salt of benzoic acid, E211 sodium benzoate, is used identically. Persons who suffer with asthma may be sensitive to benzoic acid, which may also cause a synergistic reaction with the preservative E222 sodium hydrogen sulphite. The latter substance alone can also cause reactions in asthmatics and is matched in its effects by E223 to E227, the sulphur dioxide 'group'. Some of these substances can cause contact dermatitis and a numbing sensation in the mouth when taken in substantial amounts, but in the small amounts used typically in drinks they are unlikely to stimulate such a reaction. Persons who suffer with recurrent urticaria (nettle-rash) may also be sensitive or allergic to benzoic acid or sodium benzoate. The human body excretes benzoic acid as hippuric acid, normally within twenty-four hours – there is no evidence that it accumulates in the body. The results of a trial carried out by a team of scientists at the Hospital for Sick Children at Great Ormond Street, London, suggest that BENZOIC ACID MAY TRIGGER MIGRAINE ATTACKS SYNERGISTICALLY. Following the institution of a diet eliminating the substance, seventy-eight out of eighty-eight children were cured of migraine, a success rate of ninety-three per cent. Some children who had previously suffered fits were also cured, according to a report of the trials which was entitled 'Is Migraine Food Allergy?', published in *The Lancet* in October 1983. The tests, in which benzoic acid was also combined (independently) with the 'coal-tar' dyes E102 tartrazine and E110 sunset yellow, were carried out under the direction of Professor John Soothill, a paediatric immunologist. Where the substances were combined, effects were noted in the children, but not when they were administered singly (migraine tests), the results indicating that synergistic processes had been responsible for migraine attacks.

Food-producers may use E211, E212 or E213 where E210 is approved, all of which may show similar effects upon drinkers.

E211 *sodium benzoate: See* E210

E212 *potassium benzoate: See* E210

E213 *calcium benzoate: See* E210

E216 *propyl para-hydroxybenzoate*
An ester of benzoic acid, this substance is used as an anti-microbial agent in beer and cider in the final container. It is thought that it may cause contact dermatitis, but few cases have been reported.

E218 *methyl 4-hydroxybenzoate*. Similar effects to those of E216.

E220 *sulphur dioxide* (including additives E221–7)
Produced by the combustion of sulphur or gypsum. The Romans knew of and exploited the preservative qualities of sulphur dioxide. Its use in winemaking and brewing is widespread. In wine it acts as both anti-oxidant and preservative, enhancing the wine's colour. Its principal degrading effect is upon foodstuffs containing vitamin $B_1$, which is destroyed due to the action of disulphides upon protein molecules. Because it inactivates enzymes, it is useful in arresting the malting process, where enzymes might otherwise be carried through to the fermentation stage. Some people report unusually severe hangover symptoms after consuming red wine which they believe to contain high concentrations of the preservative, pointing to a 'sulphur' taint in the flavour. It is used in very small amounts in beer and cider. Its established effects are mainly upon asthmatics and people who suffer with recurrent urticaria (nettle-rash), and in this respect it is probably the most reactive additive now in use. When inhaled (which can occur when a drink containing sulphur dioxide is being swallowed), it can precipitate an asthmatic attack. Other drinkers may experience gastric reactions to swallowing the additive, due to the liberation of sulphurous acid. Similar effects apply to the sulphites, which are salts of sulphurous acid grouped under E nos 221–7 and in particular E223 or E224, the metabisulphites which form part of many home winemaking and home brewing kits. Inhalation of E224 vapour can cause severe bronchial irritation; many home brewers and winemakers suffer this effect while preparing the material for the sterilizing of containers, using boiling water.

E260 *acetic acid*
Produced synthetically from a methanol (methyl alcohol) base derived from mineral oil (crude oil) or gas. Its use in brewing and distilling is confined mainly to the malting stage, where it is used to prevent or control convertible starch losses from the barley acrospires. It may also be used to adjust the pH of a wort, must or distilling malt slurry prior to fermentation, or as a mild bactericide in the completed drinks. No

undesirable effects upon drinkers are known. This substance is a natural constituent of sour beer, cider or wine (i.e. as vinegar).

### E270 *lactic acid*
Occurs naturally in sour milk but is produced industrially by the controlled fermentation of carbohydrates derived from potatoes and molasses, the ferment being carried out by a bacillus, not a fungus (yeast). It is used as a preservative in many drinks, especially soft drinks.

### E300 *ascorbic acid (vitamin C)*
Manufactured by biological synthesis. Vitamin C occurs naturally in fruit and green vegetables. It is used extensively in lager, wine and cider as an anti-oxidant (in wine mainly as a colour stabilizer) and especially in bottled drinks when small amounts of air enter at the bottling stage. Although ascorbic acid is essential for healthy bones, skin, gums and teeth, large intakes may cause diarrhoea and dental erosion. Susceptible persons may also develop kidney stones where there is a high regular intake.

### E330 *citric acid*
A naturally occurring substance found in many fruits, but produced industrially by the fermentation of molasses. In the misleading list of so-called 'dangerous additives' (the Villejuif List) which has been circulating in Britain for some years, citric acid is incorrectly described as carcinogenic. This substance is an irritant when used in large quantities. It is used in brewing and distilling to inhibit starch losses from germinating barley, but its major use is in home brewing, where it is recommended for many pH adjusting functions. However, it is unsuitable for this purpose because its use leaves a 'fruity' taint in the drink.

### E332 *triPotassium citrate*
This potassium salt of citric acid is used mainly as an anti-oxidant in wine in the bottle. No adverse affects are known.

### E333 *triCalcium citrate*
A calcium salt of citric acid. This substance is used as an acid buffer in wine in the bottle, sustaining the pH (acid/alkali balance) and the effects of tannin upon the flavour, giving the wine 'bite'. Buffers resist pH changes despite the addition of more acid or alkali. Wine is considerably more acid at the drinking stage than beer.

### E338 *ortho phosphoric acid*
Manufactured by one of two processes: directly from phosphate ore, followed by purification or by electrothermal extraction. It is used principally as a synergist – that is, to increase the effect of another additive, such as an anti-oxidant. It may also be used to control barley germination rate or to adjust the pH factor of a wort prior to fermentation. No adverse effects upon drinkers are known. Also used in some breweries for acid-washing of yeast.

**353** *metatartaric acid*
This additive, which is prepared from tartaric acid (E334), is used in wine to precipitate excess calcium prior to the ferment. Its source, tartaric acid, is a natural constituent of grape juice. Metatartaric acid functions as a sequestrant – that is, a selective mineral-remover.

**E401** *sodium alginate*
Prepared from certain seaweeds, especially the species Laminaria. It is the sodium salt of E400 alginic acid and is widely used among both commercial and home brewers as a copper-fining medium – it is boiled in the 'copper' with the hopped wort as a preliminary fining-agent, carrying down proteins which might otherwise cause haze-formation. Home brewing supplies shops package and sell large quantities of E401 as Irish Moss, although it is possible that E407 carrageenan is sometimes substituted. Unlike sodium alginate, which appears to be safe in use in beer, degraded carrageenan is not suitable, due to its molecular structure. Sodium alginate is also a component of some proprietary indigestion mixtures.

**E405** *propane-1, 2-diol alginate (propylene glycol alginate)*
Derived from the same seaweeds as E401, this substance is the propylene glycol ester of alginic acid. This is probably the most used beer additive in the world, especially in light beers and certainly in all lagers produced commercially in Britain, where it functions as a head-retaining agent. It helps to compensate for poor head-retention in brews which contain few hops and little malt, both of which encourage good 'natural' head-retention by adding proteins. The effects of E405 can be observed in the persistent, slimy-looking foam which clings to the side of the drinker's glass for some time after it has been emptied. No adverse effects are known, but that is not surprising in view of the fact that there have been no reports of E405's being tested in Britain for carcinogenicity, mutagenicity or long-term toxicity, although short-term toxicity tests have been conducted on laboratory animals. An ADI (Acceptable Daily Intake) was set for E405 by the World Health Organization body JECFA (Joint Expert Committee on Food Additives) in 1973, amounting to a maximum of 25 mg of the substance per kilo of body weight, i.e. the consumer's. In its 1978 report, the FACC set an interim ADI of 100 mg per litre of beer.

**E414** *gum arabic*
A dried gum from the Acacia senegal tree and the most water-soluble of all the industrially used vegetable gums. It is used mainly in beer, either as a copper-fining medium (boiled with the hopped wort, like E401 sodium alginate) or as a head-retaining agent (like E405 propylene glycol alginate). Extensive tests have been carried out on gum arabic, showing that it is largely broken down in the human colon and poses no apparent risks to health. Gum arabic is also used in soft drinks as a heading-agent stabilizer.

### 500 *sodium carbonate*

Derived mainly from sea water via electrolytic processes, although it occurs naturally in alkaline lakes. It is used mainly to balance pH during barley germination. No adverse effects are known.

### 507 *hydrochloric acid*

Sodium chloride (salt) and sulphuric acid are interacted to produce hydrochloric acid industrially. Used in brewing in a similar capacity to sulphuric acid (see 513). Hydrochloric acid is a natural constituent of human stomach juices, aiding the breaking down of food during digestion.

### 513 *sulphuric acid*

Prepared principally by the contact process, where sulphur is burned to produce sulphur dioxide gas. Sulphuric acid is an inorganic acid – that is, it contains no carbon atoms, and although public opinion considers it to be a highly toxic substance, it is essential to consistency of product at commercial breweries and is an ideal pH correcting acid in brewing. Sulphuric acid used to correct sweet wort pH is deposited as sulphate during the boil stage. Special precautions must, however, be exercised when handling 513. Highly corrosive in its undiluted state, in the amounts used in beer it is unlikely to cause harm.

### 516 *calcium sulphate (Plaster of Paris or gypsum)*

This is a naturally occurring mineral, the principal sources being France and the USA. It is widely used to treat liquor (water) before brewing, either alone or with 518 magnesium sulphate (epsom salts). This process is known as 'Burtonization' because it attempts to duplicate the well-water composition at Burton-on-Trent, this water being ideal for the brewing of bitter beers. It may be added in large quantities at either the mashing or boiling stage, due to its relative insolubility in water, or to the hopped wort prior to fermentation. Home brewing preparations described as 'Burton salts' or 'pale ale salts' often contain 516 and 518 as well as calcium chloride and sodium chloride (table salt). 'Mild ale' salts often contain 508 potassium chloride, potassium hydrogen sulphate and both 516 and 518. These minerals are all considered safe in the quantities in which they appear in commercial beer, but potassium chloride can have a diuretic effect upon some people – it may stimulate kidney and bladder activity.

### 518 *magnesium sulphate (epsom salts)*

Derived from sea water and limestone caves, this is a naturally occurring substance, used mainly for 'Burtonization' (see 516). It may have a laxative effect upon some people, but in commercial beer it is unlikely to be present in sufficiently large quantities to trigger this effect. Epsom salts were formerly the dry residue of mineral waters from springs at Epsom, Surrey.

**524 *sodium hydroxide (caustic soda)***
Manufactured mainly by electrolysis of sea water, this substance is used
to adjust pH factor at the germinating of barley or malting stages, in both
brewing and distilling. No adverse effects are known in the
concentrations permitted in drinks.

**536 *potassium ferrocyanide***
This substance is a by-product of coal-gas manufacture. It is used 'in
tandem' with zinc sulphate heptahydrate, the two combined causing a
blue precipitate, containing suspended iron and copper, to fall to the
bottom of the initial fermenting-container. The process, which is
confined to wine-production, mainly white wine, is termed 'blue fining'.
Although potassium ferrocyanide is of low toxicity, ferrocyanides, like
nitrates and nitrites, are classed as metahaemoglobinants, meaning that
they are capable of converting haemoglobin in red blood corpuscles from
the ferrous to the ferric states. In the ferric state, haemoglobin is
incapable of transporting oxygen, which could cause anaemia and
associated symptoms, including shortness of breath and dizziness. This
additive is banned in Germany and the USA.

**551 *silicon dioxide***
Found naturally as the principal component of sand, with quartz.
Combined with isinglass finings, it is used to aid the clearing of beer,
mainly real ale, and wine. It acts upon proteins, causing them to
flocculate (form into clumps) and fall to the bottom of the cask. It is also
used, in its form as aqueous silica solution, as a direct filter agent for
green beer or young wine. This substance is inert, so effects upon
drinkers are unlikely.

**558 *bentonite***
This material is derived from clay deposits in the USA and is also known
as 'soap clay'. Its use is principally as a fining (clarifying) agent in wine
and green beer, especially lager, where it may be used in a ratio of
1:1,000 (i.e. 1 part bentonite to 1,000 parts beer) or 1 ppt (parts per
thousand). The electrical polarity of bentonite particles is opposite to that
of lager and wine yeast cells, causing the yeast cells to be attracted to the
bentonite and carried to the floor of the container. This material is in
widespread use by lager-brewers and winemakers. Its aluminium
content may be responsible for identification of the metal in samples of
beer.

**559 *kaolin***
A powdered clay derived from granite. Used similarly to bentonite.

**900 *dimethylpolysiloxane* (also known as simethicone or dimethicone)**
Used principally as a foam-control agent in brewing, this additive is
often combined with a silicon gel or silicon dioxide. The additive may
contain formaldehyde, a possible carcinogen. Used as a food additive,
dimethypolysiloxane may legally contain up to 1,000 mg of

formaldehyde per kilo of food, e.g. keg lager or keg ale. In general, its use in drinks is confined to lagers and ales which have been produced in conical fermenters. Other foam-control agents include E471 glyceryl monostearate and E491 sorbitan monostearate.

## ADDITIVES WITH NO NUMERICAL ALLOCATION

*Acesulfame potassium* (or Acesulphame K)

A high-intensity synthetic sweetener, related chemically to saccharin, possessing a sweetening power 200 times that of sugar, ounce for ounce. Unlike aspartame (see below) it has a relatively bitter after-taste and is therefore often used *with* sugar in the soft drinks in which it appears, or it may be combined with aspartame. Acesulphame K is manufactured by the American chemicals company Hoechst, and it was first commented upon by the JECFA in 1981. This committee said that it was not satisfied as to its safety in food, because there was evidence that it might increase rates of lung cancer in rats. Further data was called for, and in 1982 the FACC considered the sweetener, referring to the details of thirty-four individual studies, none of which was published, though they were cited by the Committee on Toxicity (CoT) in its response to the FACC. The FACC discounted the worries about toxicity in the rat, and after the CoT placed acesulphame K in its Group A (acceptable for use in food), the FACC recommended that it should be permitted in British foods from 1983 onwards. It is a common sweetener in some so-called 'preservative-free' orange-juice drinks. In 1983 also, the JECFA announced that they were satisfied that the sweetener caused neither mutations nor cancer in laboratory tests on animals. Later (in 1985) the SCF (Scientific Committee for Food), an EEC body which is now expected to harmonize food regulatory studies prior to the wider market needs of 1992, itself deferred to the JECFA's view, but the information upon which they based their judgements remains unpublished. In the USA, however, it may soon be possible to evaluate this evidence, which could be made available under the Freedom of Information Act. So far, Hoechst has not obtained permission for acesulphame K to be used in table-top sweeteners or soft drinks in the USA, although it is widely permitted in Britain and Europe in drinks.

## Aspartame

A high-intensity synthetic sweetener formed by combining the amino-acids L-phenylalinine and L-aspartic acid. It has a sweetening-power which is said to exceed that of cane sugar 200 times. This substance is in widespread use in carbonated soft drinks and in its form as proprietary brands of tea- and coffee-sweetener, NutraSweet and Canderel. It is being used increasingly in low-alcohol and alcohol-free wines, ciders, lagers and ales. Although tests for toxicity have been conducted, these have proved inconclusive, creating a worldwide controversy about its possible effects upon consumers. In 1974, just as the FDA was due to approve its use in the USA, several independent scientists raised objections, claiming that tests had revealed that aspartame can cause mental retardation, neuro-endocrine disorders and brain lesions. An Aspartame Task Force was set up by the FDA, and the sweetener was approved for use in the USA and Britain in 1983.

The controversy hinges upon tests on rats which have been said to show that a break-down product (one produced in the body, where aspartame is 'broken down') called DKP (diketopiperazine) may cause cancer in rats. According to Erik Millstone and John Abraham*, the Task Force's report carried some interesting but crazy conclusions. At one point the following extraordinary details are given: 'Observation records indicate that animal A23LM was alive at week 88, dead from week 92 until week 104, alive at week 108 and dead at week 112.' The possibility that researchers had discovered a substance which could bring dead rats back to life seems not to have occurred to them! Such clear fudging of test results should make consumers suspicious and certainly cautious.

Professor Richard Wurtman of the Massachusetts Institute of Technology has expressed doubts about the substance and Professor John Olney also of the MIT, has conducted research which suggests that aspartame may cause chronic rather than acute brain damage, ESPECIALLY WHEN CONSUMED IN COMBINATION WITH 621 MONOSODIUM GLUTAMATE. If this is a valid conclusion, it could mean that people who regularly consume soft drinks with Chinese restaurant food may be particularly at risk. Phenylalinine may or may not be listed separately when aspartame is listed.

NutraSweet, which is owned by G.D. Searle, has been the subject of some unusual advertisements, clearly designed to construct a healthy image for the pure white powder in the minds of weight-conscious consumers. One of these ads shows an overflowing bowl of luscious fruit; alongside is the message: 'This is what NutraSweet looks like to your body. To your eyes, NutraSweet doesn't have very much in common with all these different kinds of fruit. But the rest of your body will detect a remarkable similarity. NutraSweet, you see, is made of two building-blocks of protein, like those found in foods that we eat every day. Including every one of the fruits you see here.' The 'building-blocks of protein' are the two amino-acids from which the sweetener is formed. These building-blocks are present as natural protein in much larger quantities in meat, nuts and pulses, such as lentils and chickpeas, but such foods suffer with the disadvantage that they are not as photogenic for advertising purposes!

The ad referred to above also explains that NutraSweet has been 'approved by over eighty of the world's leading health authorities'. What it does not explain is that aspartame (the generic name for the sweetener) was banned from use in foods or drinks in Austria, Belgium, France, Italy, the Netherlands and Portugal at the time it appeared.

In 1985 G.D. Searle & Co was acquired by Monsanto, the US chemicals manufacturer, which had been the major supplier of saccharin during the years of the Second World War. The NutraSweet

---

* *Additives, A Guide for Everyone* (*see* References).

Company was set up as a separate entity soon afterwards but remains under the control of Monsanto.

*Casein*

A protein derived from cow's milk, which is modified by an acid process to convert it into a colloid. It is then used to fine (clarify) wine. More than 250,000 Americans are said to suffer allergic reactions to casein.

*Kieselgühr*

An earth consisting of the fossilized bodies of minute unicellular algae, of the genus Diatoma. These fossil skeletons, which have silicified cell walls, are ground to form a fine powder, which is then used to fine (clarify) wine and beer of all forms.

*Phenylalinine*
*See* Aspartame.

*Saccharin*

The oldest of the intense sweeteners, developed in 1879. Saccharin is formed by combining oxygen with saccharic acid, which is derived from coal-tar. After many reports of opinions of its dangers, the most concentrated emerged in the 1970s, when feeding-studies in the rat showed clear evidence of carcinogenicity. Nevertheless, it is still permitted in foods worldwide, except in Canada, where it is banned. Only in the USA are makers required to indicate amounts used in foods and drinks and to carry a warning that it may be 'hazardous to health.'

*Zinc sulphate heptahydrate*
See 536 *potassium ferrocyanide.*

# DRINKS GIANTS

Throughout the world there are numerous tiny winemaking and brewing concerns, such as those in Britain, France, Germany, Italy and Spain. In the USA, Canada and Australia, microbreweries ('boutique' breweries) have increased in number since the mid-1980s, but the majority of alcoholic drinks and most soft drinks are produced and/or controlled by giant international companies or consortia of breweries. In Britain, for example, in spite of the growth of the home-brew pub 'industry', which in the 1970s began the worldwide boom in small breweries, the majority of beers, ciders and spirit drinks are produced by and for the eight large brewery groups. Between them, they own nearly half the total number of pubs in Britain and many hotels and clubs with licensed bars. This guide is not intended to delineate details of every drinks-manufacturing company in the world but to provide background material on the principal makers of familiar drinks available in the northern hemisphere, and those based in the southern hemisphere which have worldwide trading significance.

## AUSTRALIA
Two giant concerns have dominated Australian drinks-production for nearly a decade: *Elders IXL* and *Bond Brewing*. Elders' acquisition of Carlton United, the nation's largest brewery, led to the world launch of the absorbed company's Foster's Draught, a lager, which is brewed by Courage at Reading, following Elders' acquisition of the British firm in 1987. Bond Brewing, the brewing arm of the Bond Corporation, grew from the three remaining principal Australian breweries: Swan (Western Australia), Toohey's (New South Wales) and Castlemaine (Queensland). Early in 1990 mounting debts spelled trouble for the Bond companies. Nevertheless, Bond's brands, including Castlemaine XXXX lager (brewed at Wrexham, North Wales) and Swan Light (a NABLAB) continue to be brewed and marketed because of a contract with Allied Breweries (see Britain, p. 175) which expires in the next century.

## BRITAIN
Eight large brewery groups control most of the drinks-manufacturers in Britain: Allied Breweries, Bass, Courage, Greenall Whitley, Guinness, Scottish & Newcastle Breweries, Watney Mann Truman and Whitbread. *Allied Breweries*, which is itself a part of the huge Allied Lyons group, includes well-known brewery names such as Ind Coope, Ansells, Joshua Tetley, Friary Meux and Taylor Walker. The group also owns Harvey's Sherry, Teacher's Whisky, Coates Cider, Gaymer's Cyder and

174

the 800-strong chain of Victoria Wine off-licences. *Bass* is Britain's largest brewer and claims to have cornered fifty-five per cent of the national lager market with its Tennents and Carling Black Label lagers. Its company structure includes Bass Worthington, Charrington, Tennent Caledonian and Bass Ireland. One of Britain's oldest breweries, Bass was founded in 1777 by William Bass, a carrier who sold his business to a man called Pickford, so that he could concentrate on selling his ales brewed at Burton-on-Trent. *Courage* consists of three principal companies: Courage Ltd, formed in 1786 at Horselydown, South-East London, Courage Simonds and John Smith's. Early in 1986 the Hanson Trust took over the Imperial Group, parent company of Courage Ltd. In 1987 Elders IXL, the Australian drinks giant, bought Courage from Hanson Trust for £1.4 billion. *Greenall Whitley*'s best-known drink product is Vladivar Vodka, the 'wodka from Warrington'. The firm is the smallest and youngest of the big British drinks combines, although it contracted slightly when it sold Symonds Cyder to Bulmer's of Hereford in 1988. Its main brewing companies are Davenports and Shipstone and it is linked to Randall's Vautier of Jersey, by brewing its Grünhalle Lager under licence. *Guinness*, which has direct trading links with Scottish & Newcastle Breweries, has no pubs of its own but brews what is probably the most famous bottled, sedimented (naturally conditioned) stout in the world – Guinness Extra Stout. Guinness also controls and brews Harp Lager, Harp Extra and Harp Export, in a consortium with Greene King and Scottish & Newcastle. The firm also brews Budweiser for Anheuser-Busch of St Louis, USA, as does Watney (see below). *Scottish & Newcastle Breweries* consists of Scottish Brewers, Newcastle Breweries, McEwan–Younger and William Younger. The group also owns Waverley Vintners. *Watney Mann Truman*'s (the brewing arm of Grand Metropolitan) company structure includes Truman Hanbury and Buxton, Usher's, Samuel Webster's and Wilson's, Phoenix Brewery Co and Westward Hosts, as well as the Berni Inn chain and the Clifton Inns chain of home-brew pubs. Watney also brews Budweiser at its Halifax and Mortlake breweries. *Whitbread* closed two of its breweries in 1988: Chester's of Salford and Wethered's of Marlow. The firm's best-known drinks include Trophy Bitter and Stella Artois Lager, based upon a Belgian original of the same name. Through its financial arm, Whitbread Investments, the firm has acquired seats on the boards of several (smaller) independent breweries, including Fuller's of Chiswick and Morland of Abingdon. *Cadbury Schweppes* is Britain's largest soft-drinks manufacturer and, aided by its joint venture company, *Coca-Cola and Schweppes Beverages*, exports to 110 countries. Schweppes is an old firm, having been established in 1783, but the joint venture with Coca-Cola began only in 1986. Cadbury and Schweppes were merged in 1969. Arguably, since Coca-Cola is the world's best-selling soft drink, Schweppes' beverages are overshadowed, but its own well-recognized brands, such as Schweppes Indian Tonic Water, Canada Dry Ginger Ale and Sunkist Orange Crush made a major contribution to its 1988 profit of £109.1 million (beverages only). *Coca-Cola*: see USA.

## CANADA

Three companies dominate the Canadian drinks industry. *Carling O'Keefe*'s Black Label lager is brewed all over the world, including Britain, where it is brewed by Bass, and Ireland, where it is brewed at the Dublin brewery of Guinness. The Rupert Group of South Africa controls Carling, as it does Beamish Stout of Eire. *Labatt*'s best-known product is its 'Blue' pilsner lager. The firm also brews Skol, Budweiser and Guinness Stout under licence. Of the three Canadian producers, *Molson* is the largest, and its lagers are well known in most of Britain and France.

## FRANCE

Apart from thousands of tiny wine-producing concerns and hundreds of *châteaux*, the principal French producers consist of *Martell*, the 'mini' giant of Cognac brandy, and *Kronenbourg* of Strasbourg, whose Premium Lager is brewed in Britain by Courage, under licence. Martell is one of the oldest French drinks companies, having been established by Jean Martell of Jersey in 1715. It is still a family-run business.

## GERMANY

As befits the home of the Reinheitsgebot, Germany has numerous small, independent breweries, home-brew inns and several large combines, consisting of: *Bavaria St Pauli* (Hamburg), *Beck*'s (Bremen), *Binding* (Frankfurt), *Dortmunder Actien* and *Dortmunder Union* (Dortmund), *Henninger* (Frankfurt), *Kindl* (Berlin) and *Tücher* (Nuremburg). Of these, Dortmunder Union's Export Lager is probably best known outside Germany, especially in Britain, where it is a standard draught lager in many Indian restaurants, augmented occasionally by Dortmunder Kronen Classic or Kronen Pilsner. Binding is Germany's largest producer of beer.

## THE NETHERLANDS

Many 'international' lagers had their origins in the Netherlands, including Skol (which was first marketed outside its homeland in the early 1950s), Heineken, Amstel, Oranjeboom and Grolsch, but the two largest drinks producers are *Bols* and *Warnink*, whose advocaats are known throughout the world.

## ITALY

A brace of names springs to mind when Italy is mentioned in respect of drinks – *Martini & Rossi*, the firm that was founded in 1840, succeeding a former company called Martini & Sola. In addition to its world-famous red and white vermouth wines, the firm's main production centre at Pessione, near Turin, makes large quantities of sparkling wine. The largest producer, apart from Martini & Rossi, is *Peroni* of Rome, whose Nastro Azzurro and Raffo lagers are well known in most of Europe and Britain. Campari is one of the world's most famous 'bitter' aperitifs. It was created by Gaspare Campari in 1867 in Milan.

## SCANDINAVIA

Relatively strict attitudes to alcohol in some Scandinavian countries, especially Norway, mean that most drinks-production is overseen by state organizations. However, *Carlsberg* continues to dominate the area with its typically very weak and very strong versions of its Danish lagers, which are also brewed all round the world. At an original gravity of 1,030 (3.4 per cent ABV) Carlsberg Pilsner is 'probably the weakest lager in the world', while its Carlsberg Special, at 1,080 (ten per cent ABV) is unquestionably the strongest brewed in Britain, where it is produced under licence by Watney. The greatest claim to fame of Carlsberg, however, is that its research gave birth to the first reliable bottom-fermenting beer yeast, Saccharomyces Carlsbergensis, now replaced by Saccharomyces uvarum.

## SPAIN

Spanish drinks-producers, such as the sherry- and brandy-makers *Gonzalez Byass* and *Sandeman*, closely followed by *Domecq*, represent Spain's principal drinks products worldwide. Spain's numerous small winemaking concerns and *bodegas* (wine-producing estates) do not lend themselves to centralization, so the famous wines such as those from the Rioja region are not under the control of drinks giants. Only two breweries of any significant size are located in Spain – *San Miguel*, whose draught lager is widely consumed by tourists to the country (its bottled version is a popular lager in British supermarkets) and *Aquila*, whose draught lager is widely available.

## PORTUGAL

The nation which produces the only genuine port wine has no producers of port to match the size of its major foreign shippers: *Taylor*, *Cockburn*, *Croft*, *Sandeman* and *Dow*, although *Fonseca* and *Ferreira* control most of the internal markets. *Sogrape*, the largest of the indigenous wine producers, well-known for its Mateus Rosé and Dao varieties, was established in the 1860s and continues to expand.

## USA

The largest brewery plant in the world (*Coors* of Colorado), the largest producer of beer in the world (*Anheuser-Busch* of St Louis, Missouri) and the largest soft-drinks manufacturer in the world (*Coca-Cola*) put the USA into the predictably big league of drinks giants. In 1986 American brands such as *Jack Daniel*'s and *Seagrams* were the best-selling whiskeys in the world, although the USA was (and remains) the largest importer of Scotch whisky. Between them, Coca-Cola and *Pepsico* (Pepsi-Cola) control seventy per cent of the USA's soft drinks market. While Coca-Cola concentrates on drinks and is the world's largest producer of orange juice, Pepsico has major interests in restaurants, owning the Pizza Hut chain, in which Whitbread (Britain) has a stake. The remainder of the USA's alcoholic drinks business is split between the two major American wine-producers and five regional brewery groups. The wine-producer/owners are *E and J Gallo Winery Co* (San Francisco), with approximately twenty-three per cent of the market, and *United Vintners* (also of San Francisco), with about ten per cent of the market share. The principal breweries are: *Genessee* (Rochester, New York State), *Miller Brewing* (Milwaukee, Wisconsin), *Stroh* (Detroit) which also controls *Schlitz* of Milwaukee, *Schmidt* (Philadelphia) and *Yuengling* of Pottsville, Pennsylvania. The latter is America's oldest brewery, having been founded in 1829. It is still family-owned.

# Glossary of Terms and Substances

Absinthe
: A strong spirit drink flavoured with aniseed and the bitter-tasting wormwood (Artemisia absinthium). The drink was created by a Frenchman, Dr Pierre Ordinaire, in the eighteenth century. It was said to be the favourite drink of French artist Toulouse-Lautrec, but due to its narcotic residues, it was banned in France from 1915. However, its name continues in a liqueur produced by Henry Louis Pernod, which is flavoured without the use of wormwood.

Acetaldehyde
: A compound of the aldehyde group, which is formed in the drinker's bloodstream as a result of consuming alcohol. It is considered a toxin when produced in this way, but acetaldehyde is a natural preservative constituent of yoghurt. Aldehydes are important elements of flavour and are often used in synthetic flavourings.

Acid-washing
: A technique used in a brewery whereby a yeast is 'washed' in a weak solution of phosphoric acid or sodium carbonate, which is strong enough to destroy wild fungus organisms, but too weak to affect the main yeast strain, which is thus temporarily rejuvenated.

Acrospire
: The shoot or rootlet which appears from each barley grain at the germination stage. The maltster prevents the shoot from developing further by a sudden increase in heat.

ADI (Acceptable Daily Intake)
: The (supposed) daily level at which people can safely consume an additive, for their entire life span. The figure given, usually stated in milligrams of additive per kilo of the consumer's body weight, is obtained by observing a level in animals such as mice, rats and guinea pigs, at which a daily dose has no effect (NEL: no effect level) and dividing it by an arbitrary 'safety factor', generally taken as 100, i.e. one per cent of the substance.

179

Adjunct — Any grain material, or syrup derived from such material, used with malted barley for brewing. Cereals such as rice or maize and syrups such as barley and wheat may be used in some cases, either to cut the cost of the grist or to modify flavour or body in a beer, typically strong lager.

Advocaat — A Dutch alcoholic drink (about twelve per cent ABV) made from raw eggs added to spirit or wine.

Air — Public Enemy Number 1 after fermentation, but essential before it, because yeast needs oxygen in order to feed. If left for long after the ferment, beer, wine or cider will become vinegarized due to the action of an airborne micro-organism called acetobacter, which creates acetic acid from alcohol as a by-product of its reproduction process.

Air pressure — A method of dispensing beer in some public houses, mainly in Scotland, but also in some Truman (Watney) pubs in the London area.

Alcohol — One of a homologous series of compounds in which one of the hydrogen atoms of a hydrocarbon molecule is replaced by a hydroxyl group. It is also the taxable portion of an alcoholic drink and in this context exists in two main forms – ethyl alcohol (ethanol) and methyl alcohol (methanol). The English word 'alcohol' is derived from the Arabic *al kuhl*.

Alcohol dehydrogenase — A human liver enzyme capable of breaking down alcohol.

Ale — Historically 'ale' and its near-equivalent 'beer' are derived from the Danish word '*ol*' and the Anglo-Saxon '*ealu*' and '*beor*' respectively, both terms referring to an infusion of grain brewed with a top-fermenting yeast.

Alembic — An alternative name for a pot still, derived from the Arabic *al embic*.

Alginate — A substance extracted from certain seaweeds and used in many breweries in two main forms: as E401 sodium alginate, when it is boiled with the hopped wort as a fining agent; as E405 propylene glycol alginate, when it functions as a head-retaining agent, especially in lagers and keg ales.

Allergy — An adverse bodily reaction to the entry of antigens or other materials. Allergies may be lifelong, transitory or occurring only in childhood.

| | |
|---|---|
| Alpha acid | The principal bittering component of lupulin, the yellow resin found in hop bracts (cones or flowers). |
| Amber malt | A variety of malt grain kilned to a pale amber colour – now rare. |
| American barrel | A cask with a capacity equal to thirty imperial gallons (135 litres). |
| Amylase | An enzyme capable of breaking down starch. It is a constituent of human saliva. |
| Anaerobic | Literally, 'breathing without air'. Yeast is an anaerobic organism in that it can derive the oxygen it needs to reproduce and grow, in the absence of air, e.g. in a fluid such as grape juice (wine) or liquid malt (beer). |
| Aniseed | The herb Pimpinella anisum, which is used to flavour many herbal liqueurs, such as Anisette and Pernod (*see* Absinthe). A sixteenth-century writer recommended its use as 'good against belchings and upbraidings of the stomacke'. |
| Aquavit | From the Latin *aqua vitae*, meaning 'water of life', this term applies to any ardent spirit (or 'neutral' spirit) and is applied to many spirit drinks produced in Scandinavia in particular. Its German form is Schnapps and its Gaelic counterpart is *usquebaugh* which became corrupted to 'whisky'. |
| Ascorbic acid | This acid, which is better known as vitamin C, is a major additive in lagers and bottled ales and ciders, where it acts as an anti-oxidant, preventing flavour- and colour-changes. E220 sulphur dioxide is used similarly in wines. |
| Attenuation | The degree to which fermentable material is converted to alcohol and carbon dioxide by yeast. Highly attenuated wines, beers and ciders are dry-tasting. |
| Azo dye | A synthetic colouring matter which produces unfavourable reactions in some people. Azo dyes are similar to, but not synonymous with, coal-tar dyes. Neither azo dyes nor 'coal-tar' dyes are 'permitted' in alcoholic drinks. |
| Barley | A member of the graminae family of grasses, from which malt is prepared. |
| Barley wine | A misnomer, because barley wine is a high-strength ale, typically in the original gravity range 1,060–1,080 (7.5–9.5 per cent alcohol by volume)., |
| Barm | The head of froth at the top of a fermenting beer wort, and the origin of the derisive term 'barmy'. Formerly a term used to describe yeast. |

| | |
|---|---|
| Barrel | A cask with a capacity of thirty-six gallons (162 litres). |
| Beer | Any non-distilled alcoholic drink produced by the fermentation of simple sugars derived from grains or cereals. Generally taken to mean ale, stout or lager. |
| Beer-engine | The correct name for a beer handpump, which raises the drink from the cellar to the glass at the bar. |
| Bianco | The Italian word meaning 'white', often used to indicate wines of a particular Italian type, in order to distinguish them from similar red or pink forms. Generally applied to vermouth white wines. |
| Bitter | The most highly hopped form of ale, and the most popular. |
| Blanket pressure | A method of storing beer in large vats under carbon-dioxide pressure. |
| Blended wines | A term applied to wines which are mixed, by a variety of methods. Grape juices may be mixed (elderberry juice is often mixed with red grape juice for colouring), or the fermented wine may be mixed at the maturation stage. |
| Body | That quality of depth in a drink which is detected on the palate. |
| Booze | A slang term for alcoholic drinks. It is thought to be a corruption of 'bowze', a word used by medieval falconers to signify the frequent dipping of a falcon's head, as it drinks. |
| Bordeaux | A grape-growing region in France which is famed for its wines. It is also sometimes known as Gironde, its ancient name. |
| Bottle condition | *See* Natural condition. |
| Bourbon | A spirit drink indigenous to the USA, distilled from an alcoholic infusion of maize (corn). |
| Brandy | A spirit drink distilled from fermented grape juice. |
| Brewery-conditioned | Beers which are conditioned at the brewery, such as keg ale, keg lager and keg stout. Condition is induced in these drinks by carbon-dioxide top pressure. See brewing flow diagram p.74. |
| Brewster | Historically a female brewer but now used to describe judicial licensing sessions – 'brewster sessions'. |
| British sherry | Sherry produced using wine from vineyards other than those from Jerez de la Frontera, Spain. Only the fortified wines from the latter country may be termed 'sherry'. Sherries |

produced in any other country, or from any other grape source, must be prefixed by the country of origin in their title.

British wine
Wine produced in Britain from country fruit or berries, or imported grape juice concentrate. *See* English wine.

Brontë
A honey-and-herb liqueur, made in Yorkshire

Brut
A French word applied mainly to champagne, but sometimes to other wines, in all cases indicating a dry wine.

Burton
The abbreviated form of Burton-on-Trent, the 'capital' of British ale-brewing. Burton ales are mistakenly believed by many people to be beers brewed to a certain Mr Burton's recipe.

Burtonize
To add Burton water salts to brewing water (liquor) in order to brew Burton-style bitter ale. *See* Burton salts.

Burton salts
Hydrated mineral salts which are added to brewing-water (liquor) in order to brew Burton-style ale. The principal minerals are calcium sulphate and magnesium sulphate. These minerals occur naturally in the well water supply at Burton-on-Trent.

Butyl alcohol
*See* Isobutanol.

Caramel
Formerly a colouring material prepared by burning sugar alone but now derived from sugar burned with ammonia or sulphur-based substances, to achieve a high colour intensity in the materials. Brewer's caramel and some synthetic caramels are often listed simply as 'burnt sugar' and are added to beer and wine as colourants.

Carbonation
The application of carbon dioxide gas under pressure to drinks in order to give them artificial 'fizz' when drunk. The process is applied to most bottled drinks, including soft drinks, and generally to bottled ales, lagers and stouts, as well as to wine (sparkling wine) and to keg ales, stouts and lagers. The usual pressure level is 50–60 lb sq. in.

Carcinogenicity
The extent to which a substance or combination of substances is likely to induce cancer in animals or human beings.

Case
A quantity of wine, in this case(!) twelve bottles.

Casein
A protein found mainly in milk and used in a modified form to clarify wine.

Cask-conditioned
Beer or cider which is permitted to develop natural condition ('fizz') without the aid of

additional carbon dioxide pressure from an artificial source. A slow secondary fermentation takes place due to the action of residual yeast, producing carbon dioxide in the fluid. *See* Natural condition.

| | |
|---|---|
| Centrifuge | A machine in which wine which has just finished fermenting is spun at high speed. The centrifugal force thus applied, rather like that in a spin-drier, removes grape and yeast particles from the wine. |
| Champagne | A famous white wine from France. It is naturally conditioned (sparkling) wine. |
| Chaptalize | To add sugar to fermenting wine in order to increase its alcoholic strength. The process is named after Chaptal, a nineteenth-century French Minister of Agriculture. |
| Chill-filtering | A method of filtering potential haze-forming proteins from processed beers by chilling them. Agents such as certain enzymes are employed to aid the process. |
| Chocolate malt | Malt grain kilned to a very dark colour. |
| Cider | The fermented juice of apples. |
| Coal-tar dye | A synthetic colouring-matter formerly derived from coal but now synthesized in the laboratory. 'Coal-tar' dyes are implicated in certain observed cancers in test animals. The FSC (Food Standards Committee) urged caution in their use in a report of 1954. It is possible that 'coal-tar' dyes are used in some liqueurs, illegally. |
| Cocktail | A mixed drink of high alcoholic potency. Its constituents are variable, but mainly consist of a spirit, an alcoholic bitter or vermouth, a liqueur, fruit juice, ice and a cherry. It is drunk from a small glass. Cocktails were probably first concocted in Mexico in the early nineteenth century. |
| Coffey Still | *See* Still. |
| Cola (or Kola) drink | A soft drink made from an extract of the nut of the Cola acuminata, a tree native to Africa, the West Indies and South America. |
| Colloid | *See* Isinglass. |
| Condition | *See* Natural condition. |
| Conical fermenter. | A modern fermentation container in use by most large breweries and a few of the smaller concerns. It consists of a large stainless-steel cylinder tapered at the bottom and features continuous aeration of the wort. |

| | |
|---|---|
| Copper | The name for the vessel in which hopped beer wort is boiled before its fermentation. |
| Crystal malt | A light brown grade of beer malt grain, which provides colour, body and sweetness in the drink. |
| Decoction | One of the two main methods for extracting fermentable sugars (malto-dextrose) from malt grain, the other being infusion. Decoction involves heating the mixture of water and grain solids (grist), removing part of it, boiling it, then returning it to the mash tun. Decoction is employed mainly in Europe and the USA for lager-brewing. *See* Infusion. |
| Diacetyl | A treacle-flavoured substance which develops particularly in beer which is fermented at low temperatures, especially lager, and which referments slowly – hence the need for long storage (maturation) of lager. *See* Lagering. |
| Distilling | A process involving the heating of fluids in order to condense (distil) separate components of that fluid. Spirit drinks such as gin, brandy, whisky and vodka are prepared by means of this process. |
| Dry hopping | The addition to finished (fully brewed) beer of fresh, dry hops, giving the final palate of the drink a quality of bitterness different from that achieved at the brewing stage. Confined mainly to top-fermented beers (ales). |
| English wine | Only wine fermented from English-grown grapes may be termed 'English Table Wine' under EEC regulations, as distinct from British wine which is produced mainly from imported grape juice concentrates. |
| Enzyme | A protein-like substance which can act as a catalyst, i.e. it can initiate or control chemical changes in other organic substances. The enzymes cytase and diastase, which are present in the starch store contained in barley grains, initiate the conversion of starches to sugars, creating maltose and dextrose (simple sugars). *See* Synergist. |
| Ester | A compound formed when a carboxylic (organic) acid reacts with an alcohol. When, for example, acetic acid combines with ethyl alcohol (ethanol), the ester ethyl acetate and water are formed, typically in vinegar. Many esters are found in foods and particularly in fruit. They are responsible for the characteristic flavours and odours of food and are especially important in wine, contributing to the strength |

of aroma. Esters can be produced synthetically for use in artificial flavourings. The ester ethyl lactate is used in synthetic grape flavourings, and it is possible that it is used to boost the aroma of wine. Not all esters contribute to flavour or aroma; fats and oils are esters of fatty acids and of glycerol, which is a trihydric alcohol. The propylene glycol ester of alginic acid is used as a head-retaining agent in beer. Contrary to consumer-group claims that esters are responsible for severe hangover symptoms after drinking alcohol-free beers, there is no evidence that those which are used in drinks are harmful to the drinker.

Feint
The partly distilled output material of a pot still, which is fed to the Coffey or patent still for further distillation.

Fermentation
The process whereby yeast feeds upon sugars, generating carbon dioxide and alcohol as by-products.

Finings
Substances added to drinks or other fluids in order to clear them of haze, caused by material held in suspension in the fluid. The range of substances used in commercially made drinks includes isinglass, albumen, gelatin, kaolin, bentonite, kieselgühr, cellulose powder, modified casein, silica gel or silica solution, and chitin, which is derived from the shells of crabs or lobsters. Aluminium sulphate is used as a fining agent by some water companies.

Firkin
A cask with a capacity of nine gallons (40.91 litres).

Fusel oil
A mixture of acrid oily alcohols, mainly amyl alcohol, which are sometimes components of alcoholic drinks.

Gibberellic acid
*See* Gibberellins.

Gibberellins
Plant hormones, discovered in the 1960s, which control the digestion process in the barley embryo. The hormone is a component in the conversion of the starch and protein store in each grain into maltose and dextrose, the latter sugar being essential to the character of top-fermented beers (ales) in particular. Maltsters use controlled amounts of gibberellic acid to treat variable grades of malt, in order that the brewer or distiller may arrive at a consistent rate of malt extraction. Modern farming methods, using nitrate fertilizers, produce yield-oriented barley rather than brewer- or distiller-oriented forms; the use of

gibberellic materials partly compensates for this factor. *See* Malt and Nitrosamines.

**Gin**
A spirit drink distilled from a cereal infusion and flavoured mainly with juniper-berry extract.

**Gravity**
Beer, wine or cider straight from the cask tap is 'served on gravity'. Also an abbreviated form of 'original gravity'.

**Green beer**
Beer which has just finished fermenting and has not yet matured.

**Grist**
The mix of solid grains and cereal ajuncts from which a beer wort is produced. The principal material, grain malt, is milled before use, giving rise to the expression 'grist to the mill'.

**Gypsum**
Calcium sulphate in its hydrated form.

**Hallertau**
Famous seedless hops grown mainly in Bavaria, Germany, for the brewing of lager. Now increasingly used in Britain for brewing top-fermented ales as well as lagers.

**Head**
The froth at the top of a drink, especially beer

**Hogshead**
A cask with a capacity of fifty-four gallons (243 litres).

**Home-brew pub**
As its name suggests, beer is brewed, sold and drunk on the premises in a home-brew pub. Until Gladstone's Brewing Act of 1880, which introduced licensing and the checking of alcohol-content for tax purposes (it also relaxed controls over the use of ingredients, permitting non-barley cereals and sugar to be used in brewing), thousands of home-brew pubs existed in Britain. In 1700 there were 24,000, but only seven remained by 1962. Chancellor Reginald Maudling deregulated brewing in his Budget of 1963. This permitted brewing and winemaking at home without a licence, but on the condition that such home-produced drinks must not be re-sold. By 1988 the number of home-brew pubs (which are licensed) had risen to seventy-two. Although their beers are generally of very high quality and purity, these factors are no guarantee of commercial success. *See* beer surveys, chapter 3.

**Hop**
The common name for the plant species called Humulus lupulus, which is used to give bitterness and natural preservative qualities to beer. It is a member of the genus cannabaceae, which includes Cannabis sativa, a plant often sown illegally as marijuana. The hop is a herbaceous hardy perennial on a permanent rootstock, and it can send its roots down as far

as twelve feet (3.6 m) into the soil. Its principal bittering substances include tannin and especially lupulin, a bitter resin found in hop flowers. *See* Alpha acid.

Hop bine
The structure of stems and leaves on which hops grow. It is not a 'hop vine'.

Hop garden
The correct name for an area of land under hop cultivation. Also called a 'hop yard' in some areas of Britain. It is incorrect to call such an area under cultivation a 'hop field'.

Hydrometer
A calibrated float used to check the specific gravity of fluids. In its form as a saccharometer, it is used to check the specific gravity of wine and beer before and after fermentation as an estimate of alcoholic strength. The normal range of markings is 1,000–1,300, the lower mark being taken as the specific gravity of water.

India pale ale (IPA)
So called because a strong pale ale of this type was shipped by British brewers to the East India Company's staff on the Indian sub-continent in the eighteenth century. It was highly hopped and fermented with a stable yeast in order to keep it in good condition for the long sea voyage. Its fame was such that a demand for it was created at home.

Infusion
One of two main methods by which maltose and dextrose are extracted from malt grain, the other being the decoction method. Infusion makes use of the process by which one makes a cup of tea – simply by soaking the source material in hot water. Most breweries employ the infusion method for stouts and other top-fermented ales. *See* Decoction.

Irish Moss
The incorrect name for E401 sodium alginate or other seaweed-derived substances used at the boiling stage to clear beer.

Isinglass
A colloidal (glue-like) substance derived from the swim bladders of tropical fish, especially the sturgeon. It is used as the main fining (clarifying) agent in real ale and occasionally in wine. Colloids are incapable of forming a solution in a fluid and therefore act as a falling suspension, acted upon by gravity. This action carries down solid particles of material such as yeast particles. The action of isinglass may be enhanced by the use of a second colloidal material such as silica sol or silica gel. Some water companies in Britain use aluminium sulphate in a similar capacity – to make water

| | |
|---|---|
| | 'bright', i.e. clean-looking. *See* Finings. |
| Isobutanol | The isomer of butyl alcohol. Isobutanol is one of the higher aliphatic alcohols, meaning that it is a compound consisting of chains of carbon atoms. This alcohol is present in most drinks, but in much smaller amounts than ethyl alcohol. It is thought that it may be carried through to NABLABS (no-alcohol, low-alcohol beers) by the distillation process, and one expert view considers that the alcohol, which is responsible for much of the flavour of a drink, may cause hangover symptoms in allergic drinkers. It is made commercially by fermenting molasses or maize syrup. |
| Isomer | A substance identical to another in its molecular formula, but with a different arrangement of atoms. |
| Kieselgühr | A mineral powder derived from the crushed fossilized bodies of the genus Diatoma, a form of algae. It is used to clarify both wine and lager, where its electrical polarity is used to attract lager yeast cells in particular, carrying them to the floor of the container. |
| Kilderkin | A cask with a capacity of eighteen gallons (eighty-one litres), often known colloquially as 'a kil'. The term has Flemish (Dutch or Belgian) origins, as does the term 'firkin'. |
| Lager | A light-coloured beer brewed with a bottom-fermenting yeast, at a lower temperature and with less bitter hops than ales or stouts. Pilsner lager, the world's most popular form, was first brewed in the sixteenth century for Ferdinand I of Bohemia, although it was not named until 1842, when a brewery in Pilsen, in what is now Czechoslovakia, began producing beer of this type. Genuine pilsner lager must be brewed to a form of the German Reinheitsgebot, although many fake pilsners are imported, brewed and marketed in Britain. |
| Lagering | The maturing of lager, which may take up to three months. *Lagern* means 'to store' in German. |
| Lees | The sediment which forms in beer or wine during fermentation. |
| Liqueur | A sweetened spirit drink of high strength. |
| Malt | The main solid ingredient of all forms of beer (ale, stout and lager) and many distilled drinks, especially malt whisky. It is produced by steeping barley (or rarely, wheat) in water until it begins to grow (*see* Acrospire), after which it |

is again steeped ('mashed') in water at a temperature around 60°C (150°F) to yield a liquid infusion of malt, a simple sugar. An Imperial Cancer Research Fund interim report of 1989 suggested that nitrosamines in malt, and therefore in all forms of beer, may be responsible for a high risk to beer-drinkers of developing cancer of the pancreas. If long-term research supports this view, it could have catastrophic repercussions on the malting industry, which also produces large quantities of malt for the manufacture of malted drinks, bread and confectionery. Nitrosamines may be formed in the human stomach after consuming nitrites, or nitrates from nitrogen-fertilized barley. However, the risk is minimized where malt is concerned by cautious kilning of barley (see p.70), and similar levels of risk exist from hops, cornflakes (from maize), porridge (from oats) or bread (from wheat) where these cereals contain nitrate residues from fertilizers.

Mead
The oldest alcoholic beverage, fermented from honey. This liqueur-type drink was favourite of the Celts, who drank it for the four weeks following a wedding, to mark the happy occasion. This is thought to be the origin of the term 'honeymoon', i.e. a lunar month of honey-liqueur drinking.

Microbrewery
One of a growing number of tiny breweries in the USA and Canada which brew ale and lager. Most of their beers are served on 'top pressure' (aided by carbon dioxide) – the keg process – but some are bottled and naturally conditioned.

Mild ale
A beer of relatively low alcoholic strength and hop rate, normally with a sweet palate.

Moonshine
A slang term for illicit liquor (spirit), which originated in the eighteenth century. A synonym is 'bootleg liquor' in the USA, generally taken to mean illegally distilled whiskey. In the Soviet Union illegal spirit is called samogon. *See* Poteen.

Must
The mixture of grape juice and/or fruit or berry juices and sugars which forms the main fermentable material of wine.

Mutagenicity
The extent to which a substance or combination of substances is likely to induce mutation in animals – that is, a change in the genetic material (DNA), such a change being passed on to succeeding generations.

| | |
|---|---|
| NABLABs | An acronym for 'No-alcohol beers, low-alcohol beers'. |
| Natural condition | The gas condition ('fizz') which develops in untreated beer or wine which has not been processed following its fermentation. This term is generally applied to bottled ales such as Guinness and Worthington White Shield pale ale, and to champagne. Condition in cask beers (real ale) is also developed by the same natural processes. |
| NEL (No-Effect level) | *See* ADI. |
| Nitrosamines | Compounds formed when nitrites (which are found typically in cooked, processed meats) or nitrates, which may enter crops from nitrogen-based fertilizers, combine with substances called amines in the consumer's stomach. Nitrosamines are considered to be potential carcinogens (cancer-triggering substances). Nitrates can also be formed in crops or in water supplies as a result of natural organic processes, although the relatively high nitrate content of East Anglian water supplies is probably due to intense farming and low rainfall. Most of Britain's barley supplies are grown in East Anglia, but modern indirect kilning controls amounts of nitrosamines in beer and distilling barley malt. *See* Malt, above, and chapter 6. |
| Oenology | The study and/or science of wine. |
| Old ale | Contrary to its title, old ale is not necessarily a venerable beer and not always strong in alcohol. It is often a dark, sweet ale brewed during the winter quarter. |
| Organic wine | A term used to describe wines made to particular standards of cultivation and fertilization, but not necessarily additive-free. The term applies mainly to certain standards laid down in French, German, Spanish, Italian and British specifications adhered to by 'organic winemakers'. The principal European specifications, which imply the use of organically, rather than synthetically fed soils in vineyards, consist of Soil Association, Demeter and OFG1 Grade. |
| Original gravity | The brewing industry's method of assessing the likely alcoholic strength of beer, based upon its specific gravity before ('original') and after ('final') fermentation. Wine is also checked by means of og in its initial preparation stages. |

Revenue is calculated upon the revenue assessor's specific gravity tests and readings of both wine and beer.

Pale malt
The heart of good ale, stout or lager. Unlike the darker malts, pale malt contains enzymes which are capable of converting other cereals to fermentable substances, thus providing a range of flavours.

Paraflow
A series of radiating metal pipes which are used to cool hot (hopped) beer wort to the yeast-pitching temperature.

Pasteurization
A heat treatment developed by French chemist Louis Pasteur, specifically for beer – he visited several British breweries in the late nineteenth century, before publishing a treatise on the subject. The process involves rapid heating, which destroys organisms such as yeast in the drink, and is used especially to produce keg ales, lagers and stouts. Also used to pasteurize wine and milk.

Pectolase
An enzyme capable of destroying fruit pectin, which may otherwise make cider cloudy.

Perry
Fermented pear juice.

pH factor
The acid/alkali balance of a fluid. By shifting the pH of a wort or must, the brewer or winemaker can produce a higher (or lower, in the case of alcohol-free drinks) yield of alcohol in the drink. The changes are effected mainly by adding sulphuric acid in beer, or malic acid in wine.

Phylloxera
The aphid Phylloxera vastatrix, which arrived in Europe from America in the nineteenth century and devastated European vineyards. The aphid attacks the roots of vines, but American vines are resistant to it, so most modern European vineyards consist of hybrid forms, the result of grafting American stock to local types. A similar 'plague' (a fungal disease) has been responsible for a decline in the hop industry in Britain. *See* Wilt.

Piggin
A cask with a capacity of two gallons (nine litres). Now seldom used.

Pilsner (or pilsener)
*See* lager.

Pin
A cask with a capacity of 4½ gallons (20.25 litres). In its crushable plastic form, used for 'takeaway' beer, it is called a 'polypin'.

Pint
Still the standard measure glass to drink beer from, long after decimalization in Britain; its volume is equal to twenty fluid ounces.

| | |
|---|---|
| Pitch | To add yeast to a wine must or beer wort, thus inoculating it from infection by other organisms. |
| Plain | Irish term for porter (q.v.). |
| Pocket | A container for dried hops, made from porous sacking. |
| Polypin | *See* Pin. |
| Port | Port wine is Portuguese wine fortified with brandy, usually with an alcoholic strength of about 18–25 per cent by volume. By law, port can come only from Oporto in Portugal. All other port-type wines must be labelled with their country of origin, as with British sherry, Cyprus sherry etc, or must be described as 'Port-type'. |
| Porter | A dark, sweet stout with a high hop rate, i.e. it is bitter-sweet. This drink was especially popular in London in the mid-nineteenth century. An enormous porter vat in the Tottenham Court Road, London, burst in 1814, drowning seven people. Porter is now being produced again by a few of the small independent brewers. |
| Poteen/Potheen | A cereal- or vegetable-based spirit, distilled illegally in Ireland. The word means 'little pot'. |
| Prime | To add sugar to wine or beer with the aim of developing extra condition in it. |
| Pulp | The fleshy part of the grape or other fruit. Both the skin and the pulp are left in the ferment for red wine, but not for white wine. |
| Quarter | The standard measure of barley for malting. |
| Quillaia extract | A head-retaining agent derived from the bark of a South American tree. |
| Rack | To syphon a beverage from one container to another, in order to leave behind the yeast sediment. |
| Reinheitsgebot | The German beer purity law which, in theory, permits the use of only water, malt, hops and yeast to brew beer. |
| Roasted barley | Unmalted barley roasted to a dark colour and used mainly to brew mild ales and stouts. |
| Rope | An infection caused by a bacterium called zymamonas, which causes stringy threads to appear in beer or bread. This effect is the origin of the term 'ropey' to indicate something of poor quality. |
| Rum | A spirit drink distilled from a fermented infusion of molasses or cane sugar. |
| Saccharomyces | From the Latin for 'sugar-eating', the general name for yeasts. Top-fermenting beer yeast, |

which is used to brew ale, is termed Saccharomyces cerevisiae, while that used to brew lager is a bottom-fermenting variety, formerly Saccharomyces Carlsbergensis, now Saccharomyces uvarum. Wine yeasts are versions of Saccharomyces cerevisiae ellipsoideus.

Saccharometer   The brewer and the winemaker's term for a hydrometer.

Safety factor   *See* ADI.

Samogon   A Soviet spirit drink, illegally distilled from sugar or other starch sources by home-based distillers.

Secondary fermentation   *See* Cask-conditioned.

Sherry   A fortified wine, produced mainly in Spain, at Jerez de la Frontera. *See* British Sherry.

Shilling system   Used in Scotland to code beer based upon its gross price, and tied to its alcoholic strength, e.g. '80/- ale'.

Spoiled beer   Beer which has become contaminated or infected at the brewery. The term is also used to describe beer subject to alcohol-removal, in the production of low-alcohol or alcohol-free beers.

Still   An apparatus used to distil volatile elements of fluids for drinking or for use in industry. The two main forms are the pot still and the patent or Coffey Still.

Stillage   A wooden framework designed to support casks, especially beer casks, where beer is drawn from them 'on gravity' (directly from the cask tap).

Stout   A very dark, top-fermented beer, originally indigenous to Ireland but now brewed all over the world.

Sugar   Malt is a simple sugar, but textual and technical references usually apply to cane sugar. Brewing-sugar is used at many British breweries to add strength and sweetness to beer. This form is normally prepared from maize (corn syrup) or by the acid treatment of cane sugar, which is then called 'invert sugar'.

Synergist   A substance which is capable of increasing or enhancing the effect of another substance. Many enzymes behave synergistically.

Toxicology   That department of science or medicine which deals with the nature and effects of toxins (poisons).

Tun   A general name for a vessel used in a brewery or winery.

Urethane

An organic compound, also known as urethan, ethyl urethan, ethyl carbamate and carbamic acid ethyl ester, which is found in some alcoholic drinks. It is not an additive, but occurs 'naturally' as a result of chemical changes, some of which are the result of extended maturation. Urethane is a carcinogen and is so well-recognized as such that it is often used in 'bench mark' tests upon animals, in order to estimate the carcinogenicity of other substances in 'positive control group' tests. Urethane was once used in the production of pesticides.

Vermouth

A flavoured wine which is sometimes fortified with spirit. Flavourings may be obtained from barks, flowers, herbs, spices or resins. One of the latter is employed in the Greek wine retsina, which is flavoured with pine resin. Vermouths derive their name from the herb formerly used to make absinthe (*Artemisia absinthium*), called vermut in German. The best-known vermouths are probably those from France and Italy, where their commercial roots began to grow in the eighteenth century. The strength of most vermouths falls within the range 13 to 17 per cent ABV and most are pasteurized. When water is added to some vermouths or liqueurs a herb precipitate forms, making the drink cloudy.

Verticillium wilt

The fungal disease of hops which has been partly responsible for the decline of the English hop industry. Work started at Wye College, Kent, between the two World Wars has produced a growing range of wilt-resistant hop varieties, which are also high-bittering strains. This factor has forced the industry into further decline, because less high-bittering hops are needed, compared with conventional varieties, in order to achieve the same level of bitterness in beer.

Vinegar

A condiment prepared from sour wine, beer or cider.

Wallop

An ancient name for beer, formerly applied mainly to mild ale.

Water

A fluid which does not exist for brewers, who call it 'liquor'. Nevertheless, water is the principal constituent of all forms of beer, wine, cider and perry.

Wet

A derisive term used to describe those who were opposed to the prohibition of alcoholic drinks in the USA, which lasted from 1920 to 1933. Now used to describe liberal politicians in Britain, especially those within the ranks of the Conservative Party.

Whisky/Whiskey    A spirit drink distilled from a variety of cereal infusions: malt whisky from malt, grain whiskey from a range of other cereals including oats, or from maize (bourbon). Its name comes from the Gaelic *uisge beatha* or *usquebaugh*, which means 'water of life'. The Irish spirit and most grain-produced forms are distinguished by the extra 'e' before the 'y' – 'whiskey'. *See* Aquavit.

Wilt              *See* Verticillium wilt.

Wine              The fermented juice of fruit or berries.

Winter warmer     A strong ale brewed during the winter quarter.

Wort              The liquid extract of malt and other sugars from which beer is brewed, termed 'the sweet wort' before hops are boiled with it, and 'the hopped wort' afterwards.

Yeast             A single-celled fungus organism which is able to metabolize (feed and reproduce) on sugars. It is used to produce all alcoholic beverages in their initial stages. In recent years experimenters have found new uses for this humble organism. Genetic material (DNA) is extracted from pure yeast cultures to be converted into 'super starch-degrading enzymes', which improve brewing efficiency. In the future, genes from these enzymes may be used to develop yeasts which secrete useful proteins, and interferon, the substance still thought by some scientists to have value as an anti-virus treatment, has been isolated in this way. One group of researchers has succeeded in using a new yeast strain to produce 'human' albumen, which can be useful in the treatment of severe shock and burns.

Yeast bite        An acrid flavour in beer, especially ale, caused by the ineffective removal of the top yeast crop, during fermentation.

Zentner           A measure of green hops; one zentner equals fifty kilos.

Zymamonas         *See* Rope.

## What's Missing from Dr Watson's Label?

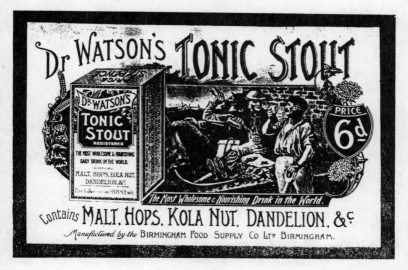

Dr Watson's set a standard in the description of a drink's ingredients which was not quite as forthright as it seems. In 1905, when this advertising placard was produced, the public view was that a long list of ingredients indicated a product of quality. On the side of the container is the explanation: 'The purity of the contents of this package are guaranteed by the proprietor.' This probably did not mean that no processing was involved, nor that no synthetic products were included, and the unanswered questions have more significance than the 'information' provided: how much of the drink is water, how much is alcohol and which part of the dandelion is used, but most important of all, what does '& ⚬' mean? One thing is certain – Dr Watson was not prepared to risk the commercially successful 'natural' image of his tonic stout by giving too much detail.

# References

## Introduction

Aitken MP, J., *Hansard* (House of Commons Debates, 16 May 1985)

BBC2 (British Broadcasting Corporation) *Food and Drink* (Broadcast 14 Mar. 1989)

*Guardian*, The, (Quoted speech by Baroness Trumpington, Minister of State MAFF, 22 Mar. 1989)

Passmore, Dr R., *British Nutrition Foundation Bulletin* (1984)

## Chapter 1

Brewers' Society, *Brewing Review* (May 1986 and Feb. 1987, Brewers' Society, 42 Portman Square, London W1)

Cobbett, W., *Cottage Economy* (Oxford University Press, 1979)

Combes, Dr R.D., 'Introduction to the Safety Assessment (Toxicity) of Additives' (*The New E for Additives*, Thorsons, 1987)

Doll, Sir Richard, and Peto, R., *The Causes of Cancer* (Oxford University Press, 1981)

Jacobson, Dr M., and Mitchell, C.P., *Tainted Booze* (Center for Science in the Public Interest, Washington DC, 1987)

National Research Council, *Diet Nutrition and Cancer* (Assembly of Life Sciences, Washington DC, 1982)

Robinson, J., *The Demon Drink* (Mitchell Beazley, 1988)

## Chapter 2

*Daily Telegraph* (18 Sept. 1989)

Fletcher, D., 'Unhealthy Sound of Silence' (*Daily Telegraph*, 12 Feb. 1987)

Graham, Dr T.J., *Modern Domestic Medicine* (Simpkin and Marshall, 1832)

MAFF, *The Food Labelling Regulations 1984* (Statutory Instrument No. 1305, HMSO, 1984)

MAFF, *The Food Labelling (Amendment) Regulations 1989* (Statutory Instrument No. 768, HMSO, 1989)

*Royal College of Physicians Report 1986, The Medical Consequences of Alcohol Abuse* (Tavistock Publications, 1987)

## Chapter 3

Brewers' Society, *Brewing Review* (Feb. 1987, Brewers' Society, 42 Portman Square, London W1)

## Chapter 5

*European Communities Official Journal*, 'Oenological Practices' (Annex III, EEC Regulation 337.79, 1979)

## Chapter 6

*Food Standards Committee Report on Colouring Matters* (FSC/PVT, REP 3., HMSO, 1954)

## Chapter 9

HMSO, *The Natural Mineral Waters Regulations 1985* (Statutory Instrument No. 71)
Jacobs, M., 'Spa Water', *Collier's Encyclopedia* (New York, 1983)
*Natural Mineral Waters* (EEC Directive 80/777/EEC, 1980)

## Appendix 1

MAFF, *Food Additives and Contaminants Committee's Report on the Review of Additives and Processing Aids used in the Production of Beer* (FAC/REP/26, HMSO, 1978)
MAFF, *Interim Report of the Review of the Colouring Matter in Food Regulations 1973* (HMSO, 1979)
MAFF, *Final Report of the Review of the Colouring Matter in Food Regulations 1973* (FdAC/REP 4, HMSO, 1987)

## Appendix 2

Egger, J., Wilson, J., Carter, C., Turner, M., Soothill, J., *Is Migraine Food Allergy?* (*Lancet*, 1983)
Millstone, E., and Abraham, J., *Additives – A Guide for Everyone* (Penguin, 1988)

# Bibliography

August, P.J., 'Urticaria' (*International Medicine Supplement*, Nov. 1983)

Barr, A., *Wine Snobbery* (Faber & Faber, 1988)

Boston, R., *Beer and Skittles* (Fontana/Collins, 1976)

*British Medical Journal. Alcohol Problems* (British Medical Association, 1983)

Brown, Dr J.A.C., *Pears Medical Encyclopedia* (Pelham Books, 1971)

CAMRA, *Good Beer Guide 1987* and *1989*
  *What's Brewing* (Sept. 1987)

Cannon, G., *Politics of Food* (Century Hutchinson, 1987)

Deighton, L. (ed.) et al., *Drinksmanship* (Haymarket Press, 1964)

Doxat, J., *Booth's Handbook of Cocktails* (Pan Books, 1977)

Eddy, P., and Walden, S., *The Cocaine Wars* (Arrow, 1989)

Elkington, J., and Hailes, J., *The Green Consumer Guide* (Victor Gollancz, 1989)

Filmer, R., *Hops and Hop Picking* (Shire Publications, 1982)

Gaman, P., and Sherrington, K.B., *Science of Food* (Pergamon Press, 1981)

Hackwood, F.W., *Inns, Ales and Drinking Customs of Old England* (Bracken Books, 1985)

Hallgarten, F., *Wine Scandal* (Weidenfeld & Nicolson, 1986)

Hanssen, M., with Marsden, J., *The New E for Additives* (Thorsons, 1987)

Hern, A., *What are You Drinking?* (Ventura Publishing, 1982)

ICI Fertilisers, *What is the $NO_3$ doing in my $H_2O$?* (ICI, 1989)

Jackson, M., *International Beer Guide* (Henri Wintermans/Mitchell Beazley, 1986)

Johnson, H., *Pocket Wine Book* (Mitchell Beazley, 1989)

Kitton, D., *Traditional Cider Directory* (Alma Books, 1987)

Kitton, D., *Good Cider Guide* (CAMRA, Alma Books, 1988)

*Living Today*, 'Sensible Drinking' (J. Sainsbury, Stamford Street, London SE1, Oct. 1987)

MAFF, *Food Additives – The Balanced Approach* (Oct. 1987)

MAFF, Food Surveillance Paper No. 8: 'Survey of Arsenic in Food' (HMSO, 1982)

MAFF, Food Surveillance Paper No. 10: 'Survey of Lead in Food' (HMSO, 1982)

*McGraw-Hill Dictionary of Scientific and Technical Terms* (1974)

Miller, J., *The Body in Question* (Jonathan Cape/Vintage Books, 1982)

Millstone, E., and Abraham, J., *Additives – A Guide for Everyone* (Penguin, 1988)

Mitchell, C., and Wright, I., *The Organic Wine Guide* (Mainstream Publishing, 1987)

Monckton, H.A., *The Story of British Beer* (Publishing and Literary Services, 1987)

Peters, Dr T., 'Free Radicals and Disease', Biochemistry Society Symposium (Reported in *Laboratory News*, Feb. 1989, Maclaren Publishers)

Reay-Smith, J., *Discovering Spanish Wine* (Robert Hale, 1976)

Royal College of Physicians Report, *Alcohol – A Great and Growing Evil* (1986)

Royal College of Practitioners, *Alcohol – A Balanced View* (1986)

Singer, Dr P., *Animal Liberation* (Avon/Discus, 1977)

Vandyke-Price, P., *Dictionary of Wines and Spirits* (Peerage Books, 1986)

Wedzicha, B., 'Sulphur Dioxide in Foods' (*British Nutrition Foundation Bulletin*, 1984)

*Which?*, Consumers' Association (May 1986 and July 1989)

Wine and Spirit Association, *Social Aspects of Alcohol* (Winter 1988)

Wood, F., 'Caramel Colours Under Review' (*British Nutrition Foundation Bulletin*, 1982)

Details of MAFF/HMSO reports and regulations reproduced by permission of the controller of Her Majesty's Stationery Office.

# Index